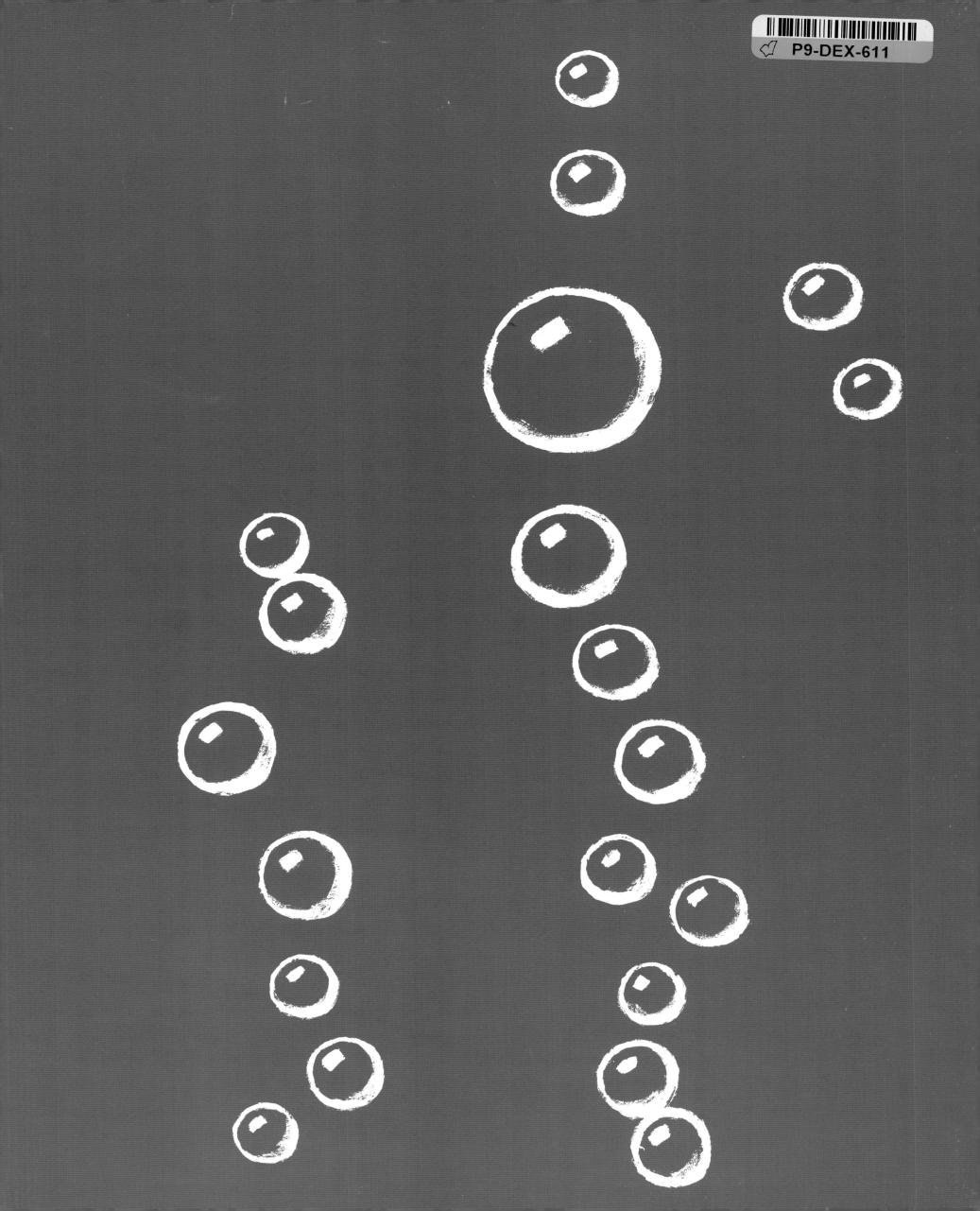

To Nicholas & Jonah
–G.A

Extra big thanks to Mandy & Jemima
–love from David

Other books by Giles Andreae
and David Wojtowycz:

Cock-a-doodle-doo! Barnyard Hullabaloo

Dinosaurs Galore!

Rumble in the Jungle

tiger tales
an imprint of ME Media, LLC
202 Old Ridgefield Road
Wilton, CT 06897
tiger tales hardcover edition published in 2001
tiger tales paperback edition published in 2002
First published in the United States 1998
by Little Tiger Press
Originally published in Great Britain
by Orchard Books, London
Text ©1998 Giles Andreae
Illustrations ©1998 David Wojtowycz
Hardcover edition ISBN 1-58925-000-1
Paperback edition ISBN 1-58925-366-3
Large Format Edition ISBN-10: 1-58925-924-6
Large Format Edition ISBN-13: 978-1-58925-924-9
Printed in China
SCP0510
1 3 5 7 9 8 6 4 2

Library of Congress Cataloging-in-Publication Data

Andreae, Giles, 1966-
  Commotion in the ocean / Giles Andreae ; illustrated by David Wojtowycz.
      p. cm.
Summary: A collection of silly verses about various creatures that live in the ocean, including crabs, swordfish, whales, and polar bears.
  ISBN 1-58925-366-3 (pbk.)
  ISBN 1-58925-000-1
  1. Marine animals—Juvenile poetry. 2. Ocean—Juvenile poetry. 3. Children's poetry, English.
[1. Marine animals—Poetry. 2. English poetry.] I. Wojtowycz, David, ill. II. Title.
  PR6051.N44 C66 2001
  821'.914—dc21
                        2001004604

Commotion in the Ocean

by Giles Andreae

Illustrated by David Wojtowycz

tiger tales

Commotion in the Ocean

There's a curious commotion
At the bottom of the ocean.
I think we ought to go and take a look.

You'll find every sort of creature
That lives beneath the sea
Swimming through the pages of this book.

There are dolphins, whales, and penguins,
There are jellyfish and sharks,
There's the turtle and the big white polar bear.

But can you see behind the wrecks
And in between the rocks?
Let's take a look and find who's hiding there. . . .

Crab

The crab likes walking sideways
And I think the reason why
Is to make himself look sneaky
And pretend that he's a spy.

Turtles

We crawl up the beach from the water
To bury our eggs on dry land.
We lay a whole batch,
And then when they hatch,
They scamper about in the sand.

pitter patter

pitter patter

squeak
squeak

click click

Dolphins

The wonderful thing about dolphins
Is hearing them trying to speak.
It's not "How do you do?"
As I'd say to you.
It's more of a "Click-whistle-squeak!"

whistle

click

Angelfish

Hello, I'm the angelfish, darling,
The prettiest thing in the sea,
What a shame there are no other creatures
As gorgeous and lovely as me!

jiggle jiggle

jiggle

Jellyfish

The jellyfish just loves to jiggle
Which other fish think is quite dumb.
She knows that it's not all that useful
But jiggling's lots of good fun.

Shark

I swim with a grin up to greet you,
See how my jaws open wide.
Why don't you come a bit closer?
Please, take a good look inside. . . .

Swordfish

I love to chase after small fishes,
It keeps me from getting too bored.
And then when I start feeling hungry,
I skewer a few on my sword.

tickle
tickle

Octopus

Having eight arms can be useful,
You may think it looks a bit funny,
But it helps me to hold all my children
And tickle each one on the tummy.

tee
hee!

bzzz

bzzz

Stingray

At the bottom of the ocean
The stingray flaps his wings.
But don't you get too close to him,
His tail really stings!

Lobster

Never shake hands with a lobster.

It isn't a wise thing to do.

With a clippety-clap

And a snippety-snap,

He would snip all your fingers in two.

Snippety snap

Clippety clap

Deep Sea

Miles below the surface
Where the water's dark and deep,
Live the most amazing creatures
That you could ever meet.

There are fish of all descriptions,
Of every shape and size.
Some have giant pointy teeth
And great big bulging eyes.

Some of them can walk around
And balance on their fins.
But the strangest fish of all
Have glowing whiskers on their chins!

Blue Whale

There's no other beast on the planet
As big as the giant blue whale.
He measures a massive one hundred feet long
From his head to the tip of his tail.

Walruses

Our bodies are covered with blubber
And our tusks are incredibly long.
We're grumpy and proud
And we bellow out loud
To show that we're mighty and strong.

Uuurggh

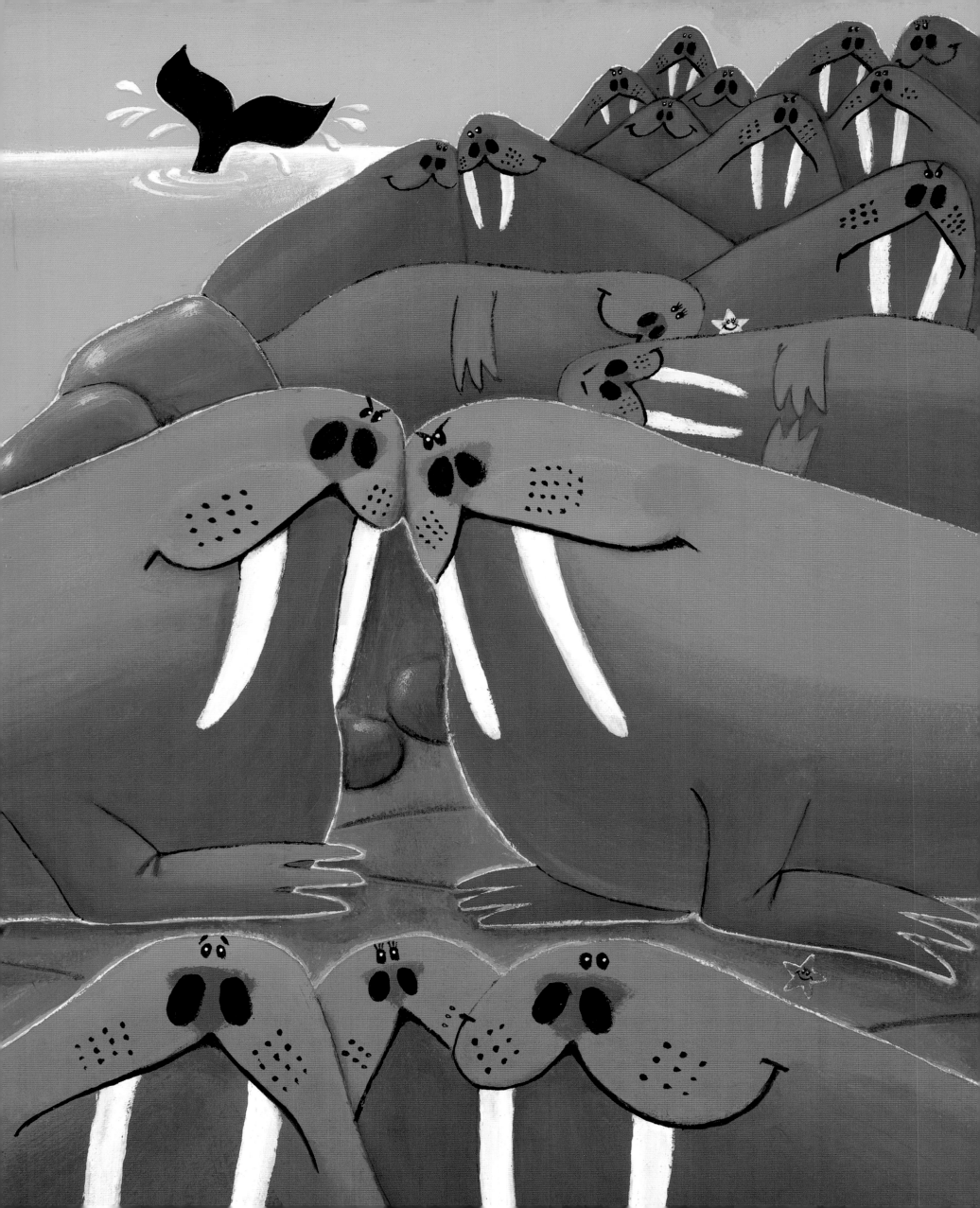

Wheeee!

splish

splash

splosh

Penguins

We waddle around on our icebergs,
Which makes our feet slither and slide.
And when we get close to the water,
We leap with a splash off the side.

Polar Bears

Deep out in the Arctic
The mommy polar bear
Snuggles up with all her children
Since it's very cold out there.

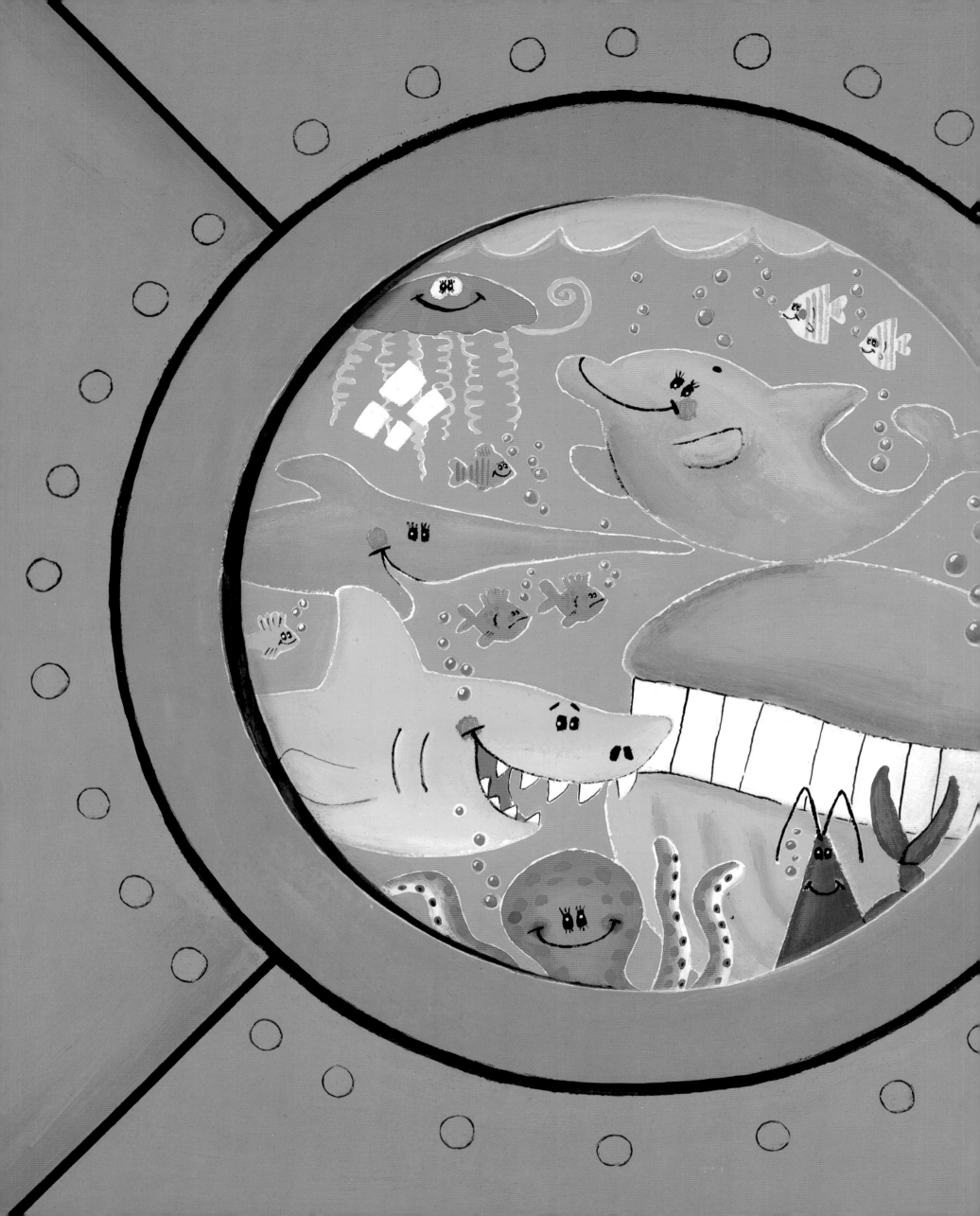

What a lot of creatures
We have seen beneath the sea,
What a lot of funny things they do.

Some of them might lick their lips
And eat you in one bite,
And some might want to swim around with you.

The dolphin's very friendly
And the lobster's very fierce,
But the shark is the most dangerous by far.

Can you name the other friends
We've made along the way?
See if you can tell me who they are.

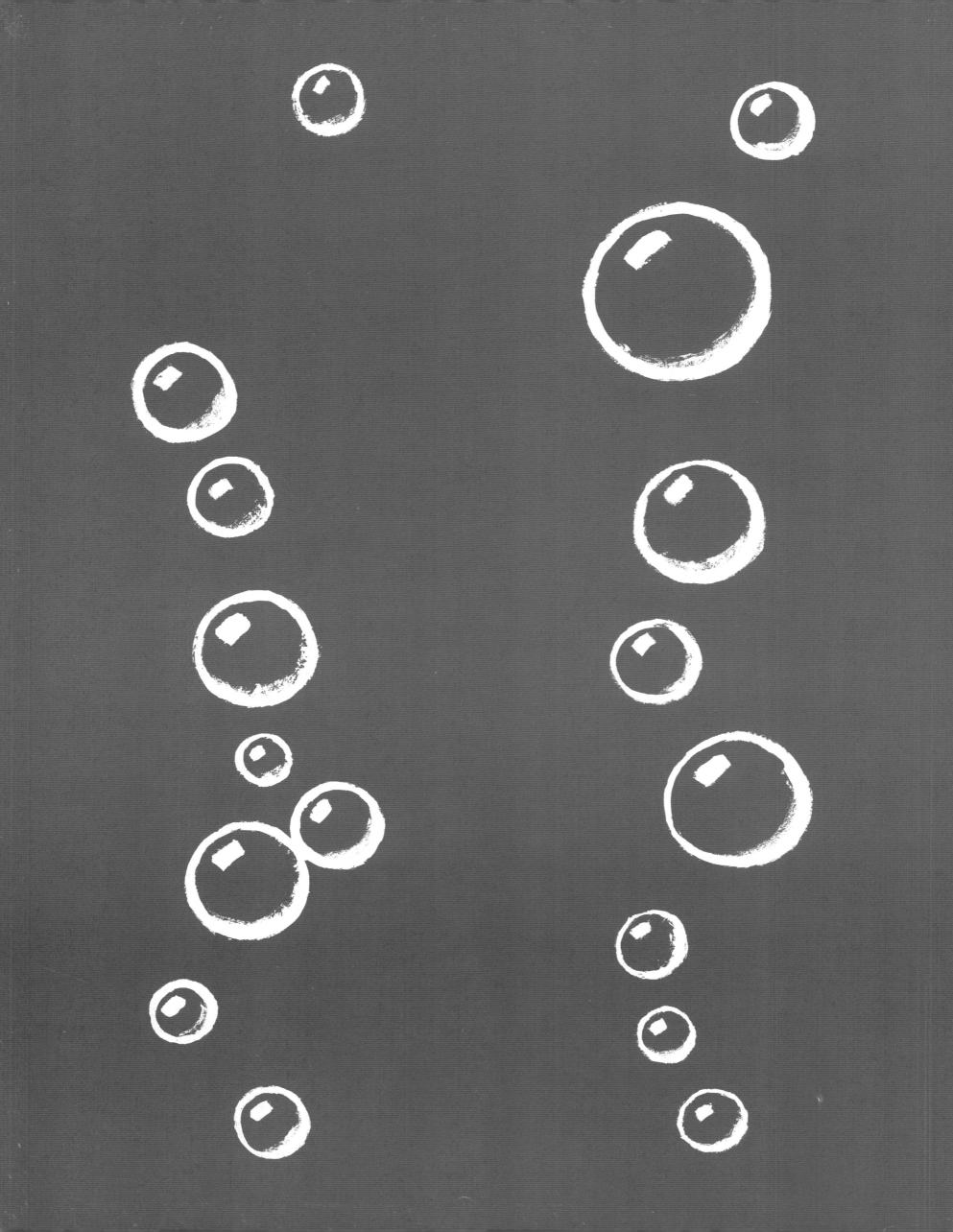

Joan Miró, in all of a lifetime's work, seems to remind us that play is one of the essential human activities and should not be treated as something merely frivolous. Certainly there are games that have, or almost have, neither rhyme nor reason, but there are others—like the one that, in the most varied forms, Joan Miró, faithful to himself as much as to others, has carried on as a stubborn pioneer—that bring to mind without seeming to just what our presence in the world implies for us that is serious and quite clearly fundamental. Joyous test of keen-witted agility for young girls and boys, our game of hopscotch, whose leftover markings sometimes liven up the gray dullness of our sidewalks, is it not expressly placed under the double sign of Heaven and Hell? —MICHEL LEIRIS

GUY WEELEN

Translated from the French by Robert Erich Wolf

HARRY N. ABRAMS, INC., PUBLISHERS, NEW YORK

Editor: Lory Frankel
Designer: Judith Michael

Frontispiece:
Woman with Three Hairs Surrounded by Birds in the Night. Palma,
2 September 1972. Oil on canvas, 95⅞ x 66½″ (243.5 x 168.9 cm).
Collection, The Museum of Modern Art, New York. Gift of the
artist in honor of James Thrall Soby

LIBRARY OF CONGRESS CATALOGING-IN-PUBLICATION DATA

Weelen, Guy.
Joan Miró.

Bibliography: p. 185
Includes index.
1. Miró, Joan, 1893–1983. —Criticism and
interpretation.   I. Title.
N7113.M54W4413   1989   709′.2′4   88–7816
ISBN 0–8109–1536–7

A TIMES MIRROR COMPANY

Printed and bound by TLP,
Ljubljana, Yugoslavia

CONTENTS

1. Joan Miró

INTRODUCTION

The campaign the Surrealists launched as far back as the end of World War I (counting the time it was in gestation) is undoubtedly the one that has most deeply challenged our society's individual and collective way of thinking. It swept rapidly across national boundaries to take on an international character. More than sixty years later, it still permeates many aspects of our life. Often waged to the tune of provocations and scandals, among other things it succeeded in throwing reason into doubt, in setting language adrift, in unhinging the spectacle of the streets, in breaking up whatever makes an image distinct and unified. And whatever one may think or say about that, it has had its part in letting the dream speak out ungagged.

If Romanticism had unstopped long-bottled-up energy, Surrealism, its last offshoot, did away with all restraints. Out of the intensity and lightning-like speed of our means of communication, our ways of communion, it forged a new way of conceiving the world. The student uprising of May 1968 in Paris was a Surrealist happening as well: "Here we spontane" and "The dream is reality" were scribbled on the walls of Censier, one of the university buildings, while "Imagination seizes Power" embellished the staircase of the Political Science building.[1] To its great credit, Surrealism, in the wake of Sigmund Freud, took on the unconscious and aimed to reunite in man what an entire rationalistic-minded civilization had done its best to keep forever parted: the things of day and the things of night.

Dormir.	*(To sleep.*
Les sommes nocturnes révèlent	*The night-time burdens [slumbers/sums] reveal*
la somme des mystères des hommes.	*the sum of man's mysteries.*
Je vous somme, sommeils,	*I summon you, slumbers,*
de m'étonner,	*to thunderstrike me,*
et de tonner.[2]	*and to thunder.)*

For highly cultivated minds, reason as warranty of civilization was—and, too often, still is—held to be man's surest means of ensuring his own development and his hold over the world. Such minds were not prepared to see a band of chilling dialecticians, of disheveled dreamers, take steps to overthrow the universal idol; whatever the cost, they had to be prevented from wreaking their havoc.

When André Breton issued the first "Surrealist Manifesto" in 1924, to a hostile and disdainful society, such a text could not fail to make revolutionaries of any who subscribed to it. Surrealism "acts on the mind very much as drugs do; like drugs, it creates a certain state of need and can push man to frightful revolts."[3] Thus Surrealists direct their fire against the establishment of smug sedentaries, and to drive it to its limits, they glorify Eros. "...the sexual relations themselves have become much more closely assimilated with social relations; sexual liberty is harmonized with profitable conformity. The fundamental antagonism between sex and social utility—itself the reflex of the conflict between pleasure principle and reality principle—is blurred by the progressive encroachment of the reality principle on the pleasure principle. In a world of alienation, the liberation of Eros would necessarily operate as a destructive, fatal force—as the total negation of the principle which governs the repressive reality."[4]

The Surrealists, confident in their position, praised perversions in order to throw reality into even greater disarray. "In a repressive order, which enforces the equation between normal, socially useful, and good, the manifestations of pleasure for its own sake must appear as *fleurs du mal*. Against a society which employs sexuality as means for a useful end, the perversions uphold sexuality as an end in itself; they thus place themselves outside the dominion of the performance principle and challenge its very foundation. They establish libidinous relationships which society must ostracize because they threaten to reverse the process of civilization which turned the organism into an instrument of work."[5]

For the Surrealists, de Sade, the "divine Marquis," was the liberating hero destined to overturn the world as it is:

He has never ceased to throw out the mysterious orders
That open a breach in the moral night.
It is through that breach that I see
The great shadows cracking apart, the old mined husk
Dissolving away.[6]

2. *Drawing.* 1944. Pen and ink

In his first manifesto Breton further declared: "Man proposes and disposes. He and he alone can determine whether he is completely master of himself, that is, whether he maintains the body of his desires, daily more formidable, in a state of anarchy."[7]

If, compared with its first upsurge, the Surrealist revolution has undergone a sea change in the course of events, if today the aesthetic attitude prevails over its original approach, this is because time has gotten the better of it, as has, no less, the reality principle. Then, too, surely it was contradictory to exalt the cult of passionate love, of the unique, superb, all-mediating woman, and at the same time to call for a sexuality without restraints. A dream lived in everyday life surely brings with it a too-cruel reality. And, after all, do we know any revolutions that have not been betrayed? The fact is ineluctable: revolution becomes null and void the moment society sets about acquiring its formerly misunderstood and rejected artworks and lets zeroes pile up after prices once counted in two figures. What remain are insurgents, people somehow still in revolt but no longer revolutionaries. What was explosive has more or less ceased to be so, and the once-seditious works are salvaged by the members of a group knowing itself strong enough to indulge that taste. Any "new meaning" in those works has long since ceased to disquiet anyone. Society, for a moment taken aback or even dumbfounded, first reacted strenuously, then made the new ideology or theory sing to its own tune. Once the new ideology or theory enters into the history of thought of its age, it more or less irrigates the field of culture until these waters, originally from a fresh source, for a time forced into a flood, trickle away in distant desert sands. Sometimes the violence of the flow leaves traces on the terrain that either make a lasting mark or slowly fade away.

It is staggering to think of the additional, perhaps insurmountable difficulties that Joan Miró would have had to cope with if, on his first visits to Paris, he had not met up with the revolutionary painters and poets linked to Tristan Tzara and André Breton. It was neither chance nor fate that led him to settle, in 1920, at 45, rue Blomet, the seething seat of pre-Surrealism. Rather, it was that subconscious force that vitalizes and acts within individuals and thus takes charge of their decisions and actions. As

Miró wrote to his friend E. C. Ricart, he felt himself moving toward such a "luminous liberty of the spirit." In any case, it is not surprising that Miró, dividing his time between Catalonia and France, arrived in Paris just in time for the first Dada events and the famous Dada festival of 26 May 1920.

The cornerstone of the entire Surrealist edifice remains the dream, in which the desires that the censoring mind blocks out can have their way. If Surrealist poets and painters welcome without control whatever presents itself to their mind and eyes, it is because such automatism makes it possible to illuminate and decode the true meaning concealed behind images that appear mysterious only because they are always metaphorical. According to Freud, one needs to see in these the complex deformations provoked by the displacement and condensation that serve to dissimulate what consciousness disapproves but which will inexorably seek to be expressed.[8] This entails, above all, spontaneity: accepting the entire mass of whatever comes to us without selection and, most important, without trying to arrange it aesthetically. In this way, ever-watchful reason and logic are prevented from imposing their power to organize. When the consequences are pushed to the extreme, as in fact was done, art no longer matters and what remains is revelation, which the Surrealists always found poetic and marvelous.

On a number of theoretical planes, Miró's particular approach was opposed to the way André Breton, the guardian of the sacred flame, understood the revolution Surrealism introduced. Yet the illusion of agreement prevailed; in *Le Surréalisme et la peinture* Breton wrote, "Miró's turbulent entry upon the scene in 1924 marked an important stage in the development of Surrealist art. His work up to that point had demonstrated artistic gifts of the highest order limited only by a certain intellectual hesitation, but now at one bound he cleared the last obstacles that still barred his way to total spontaneity of expression. From then on, his output placed on record an innocence and freedom that have remained unrivalled."[9]

For all that, it seems clear that for the long stretch between 1923 and approximately 1960, nothing in Miró's works admits the application of the terms *spontaneity, innocence,* or, even

3. *Drawing.* 1950. Watercolor on torn paper

4. *Drawing.* Watercolor on torn paper

less, *freedom.* And after 1960, when his works finally became spontaneous (whether truly spontaneous remains in question, and the question of its innocence does not arise), his art was no longer endorsed by the Surrealists. The bonds still linking him to them—over the years he did take part in several of their exhibitions—were the expression of due loyalty to the struggles, rages, and refusals of his youth, which would continue to stir him, though with a quite different vibration.

The sketches, detailed studies, preparatory drawings for a great number of canvases, and, especially, the squared-up cartoons for transfer to the final project before the laying on of color—these prove definitively Miró's total lack of spontaneity. The ideas for *The Siesta* (plates 74–76), *Queen Louise of Prussia* (plates 109–11), *The Harlequin's Carnival* (plates 70, 73), the *Dutch Interiors* (plates 94–102), the *Imaginary Portraits* (plates 112–20), and so many others took on more and more precise form from drawing to drawing. The image was worked out slowly, then polished, pruned, eventually destroyed and reconstituted in order to achieve the best formulation. Annotations on the sketches such as "painted well," "precious material," "very concentrated," and the like bear witness to the quest for a style, or at least a manner, such as was entirely out of place within the perspective of Surrealism.

And if Miró's little "stick men" look like the drawings a schoolboy might scatter through the pages of his detested Latin notebook, that is not enough to give Miró the semblance of childhood innocence. If one insisted on a source for such figures it would be not the schoolroom but the street, where people reveal their unawareness of everything except what weighs on their heart and craves to speak out. In any case, who still believes children are innocent? They may be candid, frank even, and therefore unlike grownups, but, just like their elders, they are motivated and maneuvered by profound necessities unknown to themselves. Like every creature, they seek to satisfy the elementary need for pleasure and, in tears, refuse as we do whatever smacks of displeasure—with the sole difference that adults' reactions are generally more energetic than children's tantrums. So where then is "freedom"? Where free choice? Painful —even, for some of us, unbearable—as we find it, sooner or later

we have to humbly accept that basically our psychological field is not free but determined by specific factors. And even then, freedom shows itself as an illusion—which it is—maintained in order to beguile and better deceive us.

So then, in the infinite diversity offered by the universe of forms, it would really be too much of a marvel to be able to believe that any real freedom of choice existed. In reality, what has to be discounted in advance is an act that takes place within the context of attraction, fascination, desire, and (less noble but no less certain) repetition and habit. The desire that desires constant satisfaction is a curved line, and this because it embraces the object (of its desire) yet cannot help but return to its starting point.

Let Miró deny that there is any symbolic meaning in the spiral, cone, triangle, bird, eye, star, the three hairs and three filaments, the foot, and so on found in his paintings. Say what he will, all those figures mean something. The ultimate proof is his own long use of such signs impregnated with significance and their tenacity in returning over and over again to take their place almost mechanically in his graphic repertory. Like it or not, they disclose the meanders of his familiar and profound reverie. While the metaphorical game that consists of disfiguring or obscuring those figures is certainly a defense, a plastic and poetic jugglery over which Miró possesses exquisite mastery, the disguise does not modify their meaning. On the contrary, it makes even clearer their tyranny and their potentiality. It is by just such a roundabout path, and protesting all the way, that the preoccupations of Miró's unconscious reveal themselves to us. His refusal to recognize them itself implies that despite everything he knows what dynamite he is playing with. Pierre Loeb, in his *Voyages à travers la peinture*, records Miró's seeming indifference:

"This is a horse, isn't it?"

"Yes, yes."

"But no, it's a bird."

"Yes, yes."[10]

That is how Miró, always polite, replies when asked for an

9

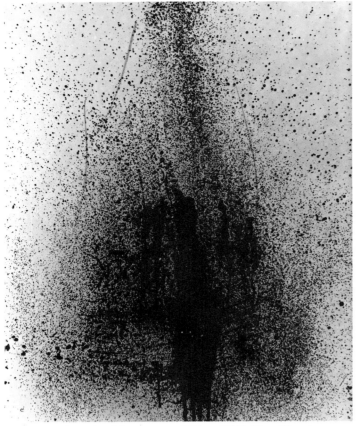

5. *Painting I/V*. 1960. Oil on canvas, 36¼ × 28¾" (92 × 73 cm)

6. *Female Bather of Calamayor*. 1960. Oil on canvas, 44⅞ × 57½" (114 × 146 cm)

explanation. Himself, he knows very well what he is doing, but he considers all discussion useless—on that plane at least, because otherwise he loves to talk seriously about painting, and he is capable of reading the most hermetic poet.

On a sketch, Miró notes: "Too erotic," which should be read as: "Too directly erotic," and the very next drawing strings it out even further. Be that as it may, the reticent Miró was often interrogated and he has replied amiably, saying many pertinent things to Jacques Dupin, Georges Duthuit, Georges Raillard, J. J. Sweeney, Dean Swanson, Yvon Taillandier, and others. His replies swim with the current, yet they lie deep. Like the cuttlefish that conceals itself in a jet of ink, Miró hides behind a cloud of necessary rationalizations and sublimations. The escape ladder, the fertility goddess, "the all-seeing eye and all-hearing ear," evoked and even invoked, do not hinder sex organs that are open (red) or closed (black), loaded with flames and teeth, from spinning around against ambiguous backgrounds of water/air that take one back to the first perceptions of life. And those forms do make signs, and we cannot help wondering what to make of them while at the same time conceding that Miró is perfectly within his rights in not caring to explain himself. If he is convinced that any such attempt is useless, there is every reason to have faith in his wisdom.

After 1960, Miró took another path in his painting; staked out long before, little by little it took shape and slowly opened up. In that final phase, he seems to have felt ever more strongly the need to suppress everything that might come between the desire and its projection, that might set brakes on expression and decision. What he discovered on his visits to the United States was to become for him a source of reflection and encouragement. He would no longer feel himself alone on his bold and unwonted course. It is equally

likely that his visit to Japan in 1966 permitted him to deepen the understanding he had already acquired of Zen thinking and, perhaps, in particular, of Japanese poetry, which, especially in the haiku form, succeeds in fusing a moment and a state of soul into a very delicate and mysterious vibration. As far back as 1936, Chinese painting and poetry had been for him a point of reference.

If he then abandoned the kind of image giving rise to Surrealist illusions, he nonetheless remained faithful to a romantic attitude that had been scoured and broadened by Surrealism. The fulgurating force of gesture, the fascinating encounter, the marvelous instant, the dazzlement of the shock all underlie his paintings of those years. However, his familiar population of irritated and teasing funny little figures did not simply go away: they took refuge in his sculpture. If intensity imposed itself on Miró as a means of relations with other people, he would seem to have relied on it more than ever in those years. He put out a violent energy whose force had to be *felt*, like the sound of a percussion instrument: immediate and absolute. In refusing to move in the habitual cultural channels, he sought to make of art something dazzling, dizzying. Nor was he ever led to look down on the means and servitudes of painting; instead, he forced them, transformed them.

Choice as such was ousted by decisions taken in exasperation or utmost lucidity, under the pressure of inward powers, and by the lightning flash of gesture, leaving only spontaneity to burst out. The splash of brush on canvas, the spray left on a ceramic tile by a broom dipped into the glaze are an instant act of love/act of poetry—and, for the unconscious, one can imagine which—in which dazzlement discharges itself. The intensity of the shock experienced, the only thing that counts for the painter, stamps the

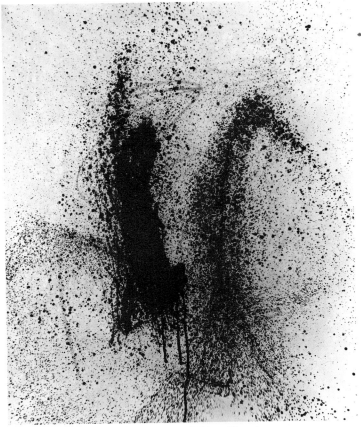

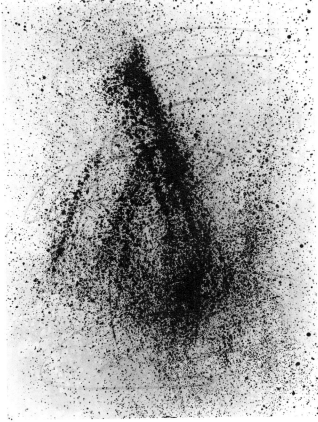

7. *Painting II/V*. 1960. Oil on canvas, 31⅞ × 25⅝" (81 × 65 cm)

8. *Painting III/V*. 1960. Oil on canvas, 36¼ × 28¾" (92 × 73 cm)

work with authenticity, and this the viewer must experience in his turn. In this way, art becomes a field where, with all rationality abolished, the body drives itself onward indefinitely to the point of exhaustion and death. No longer are there limitations, only immoderation. Miró knew that for him both art and revolt, in their violence, constituted a metamorphosis of the body. Destroy or construct, that remained the alternative: he was no longer granted means to draw back or turn back. From the first gesture, he had to find what he was after, not because he wished to but because he was trapped in that very instant: the desire of what must be created.

Out of the interrelation or, better, intermingling of such actuating ideas, Miró produced astounding works that are difficult to grasp because they are so economical. To the Western mind, the abundance of elements and propositions and their interactions among themselves are the basic sources of interest and satisfaction. Restriction of means pushed to an extreme is contrary or, at least, not natural to its sensibility. And so one scarcely knows what to think of *Blue I, II, III* (1961; plates 240, 244), *Mural Painting for the Cell of a Solitary I, II, III* (1968; plate 13), *Triptych: The Hope of a Man Condemned to Death I, II, III* (1974; plates 241–43), with its simple line and a few spots on a monochrome ground, *Painting I/V, II/V, III/V* (1960; plates 5, 7, 8) and *Female Bather of Calamayor* (1960; plate 6), or *Triptych: Fireworks I, II, III* (1974; plate 245), composed out of drops of paint, pinging like a child's glass marbles on a light surface on which some remain stuck, others drift about, still others seem to bounce back from the taut canvas.

All of this involves above everything a spatial adventure: when open, space engulfs; closed, it rejects, and then the smoothly polished fluid forms run, slip, and slide about. This curve is a trajectory against a backdrop of night, those colored particles are

galaxies, fiery tails of spinning comets traversing the immense void. Created from deliberately restricted means and a humility that borders on pride, they represent the human temptation, stripped down to its ultimate, to find its way to the atmospheric effervescences in order to dissolve itself there, become anonymous. It is anonymity that gives Miró the feeling of losing himself in himself and of attaining the universal.

If Miró did succeed in mastering this poetic *co-naissance*, this birth/understanding—and this is conceivable when one traces the development of his oeuvre—does that mean he attained true freedom? An affirmative reply would be both generous and encouraging. Long discussion would be required to envisage the problem in all its range, but one consideration does need to be stated. Culture is more than the accumulation of items of information brought into relation and offering the possibility of ever-renewed interpretations. As much as culture shapes our mind, it shapes our body as well. It inscribes itself in flesh and bone with our first sensations: a mother's caresses, the intensity of her voice, the space across which she comes to us, light caught in the cradle's curtains, moisture, the warmth around us, and all the rest. It is highly likely that we never lose such imprints and that they dispose us to carry out certain actions in a certain manner. They belong— they, too, in their general form—to an accepted code because they are traits of our tribe and our geographical situation. Even the most enlightened mind needs to defend itself against such marks and molds, so as to forestall repetition and monotony. Fashioned thus without our knowing it, even the movement we think free is disposed according to the norms of the group to which we belong. To invent others—if that is possible—is to turn against our group, to contest it: it means joining the revolutionaries' camp.

9. *Landscape (On the Shores of the River Love)*. 1927. Oil on canvas, 51⅛ × 76¾″ (130 × 195 cm). Private collection, France

At this point a question seems to arise: Did Miró have a method? What may have been his approach to the world?

In the face of the painter's disconcerting faculty of invention, one wonders if the famous letter about the *voyant,* or the seer, that Rimbaud wrote at age seventeen to Paul Demeny might not be pertinent. Without wishing to "give a class in new literature," two days earlier he had flung the first bomb at Georges Izambard:

Now I am wallowing in vice as much as I can. Why? I want to be a poet and am working at rendering myself *voyant:* you will not understand me at all and I scarcely know how to explain it to you. It involves arriving at the unknown by throwing *all my senses* into disorder. The sufferings are enormous, but one has to be strong, to be born poet, and I have recognized myself as poet. It is not my fault. It is wrong to say: I think. One ought to say: I am being thought. Excuse the play of words.

I is someone other. So much the worse for the wood that finds itself violin, and to hell with those who are simply unaware, who split hairs over things they haven't the slightest inkling about![11]

Despite the pyrotechnics of this text and its fascination for the Surrealists, it is necessary to put the fire under control: in his own life Miró seems to have ignored all disorder and derangements. What mattered for him was whipping up a tension that he refused to induce by chemical or physical means. It seems that he was rigorously incapable of achieving satisfaction by such overly agitated and show-off antics. For certain painters, silence and dogged effort are as important as colors. A single place, always the same—the atelier—permits them to live the most unimaginable adventures in front of a blank canvas. Miró was very probably one of these.

That Miró considered the fantasia of language important is proven by his play with phrases and isolated letters on his canvases as well as by various poems he wrote. Perhaps by taking all of his works and basting them together, one to the other, in long, loose stitches, one can find something in common with the method of absolute rigor, of disorder exorcised, that Raymond Roussel disclosed in his posthumous book about how he had written certain of his works. In fact, while conversing with Georges Duthuit, Miró showed himself not unaware of that extraordinary approach, which, he said, "brought...refreshing emotions."[12] Pleasure and curiosity arise from the following example, "thanks to the citations, the only classic passage in Roussel,"[13] giving forth the particulars of the problem:

1) *Baleine* (marine mammal [whale]) to *îlot* (islet); 2) *baleine* (whalebone, lamella) to *ilote* (Spartan slave [helot]); 1) *duel* (combat between two) to *accolade* (two adversaries reconciled after the duel and exchanging the accolade on the terrain); 2) *duel* (tense of Greek verb) to *accolade* (printer's sign); 1) *mou* (spineless individual) to *raille* (here I thought of a lazy student whose comrades rail at him for his incapacity); 2) *mou* (culinary substance [animals' lungs]) to *rail* (railway). These three couplings of words gave me the statue of the helot made out of corset whalebones rolling on rails of calf's lungs and bearing on its pedestal an inscription relative to the duel tense of a Greek verb [*la statue de l'ilote, faite de baleines de corset, roulant sur des rails en mou de veau et portant sur son socle une inscription relative au duel d'un verbe grec*].[14]

This long quotation may let us imagine some relationship between such verbal gymnastics, the stern discipline they presuppose, and the way Miró, by force of concentration, succeeded from 1924 on in articulating the different elements at his

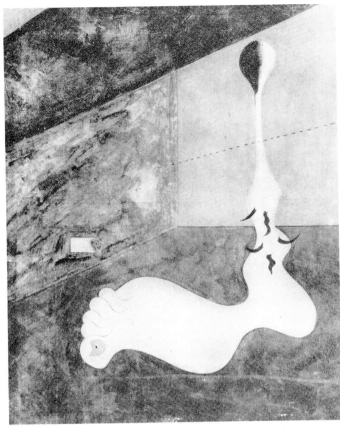

10. *The Statue.* 1925. Oil on canvas, 31½ × 25⅝" (80 × 65 cm). Private collection, Brussels

disposition: space, color, line, spot. In his works, he assigns each of these roles that are often different from their usual functions, he changes their meaning, and he makes them play a delirious game in which they are always doing something different. Whatever the theme or motif, neither Roussel nor Miró compromised with mere illusionism, even when dealing with pure description. Further, it is such unhemmed and entirely subjective associations that give Miró's titles their poetry, though those titles need to be taken for what they are: a way of going through and beyond appearances, which act on us like mirrors set to befuddle larks.

Seductive as this investigation may be, and despite the nervous excitement it rouses in the intellect, the sad fact is that the thread breaks. The forms at play in the series of *Landscapes* (1926–27; plates 9, 86–90), the small paintings on copper (1935–36; plates 141, 142, 145), the *Constellations* (1940–41; plates 159–67), the gouaches, watercolors, and drawings (1942–44; plates 168–76), the large paintings of 1945 (plates 185–87) all resist our metaphorical needle, and it slips from the fingers. Miró's works probably obey an order of imagination not so easily reducible to a rule as systematic as Roussel's.

Miró always held poetry to be essential to his life. His drugs were poetry and music. As a young man, he frequented writers and poets. In Barcelona he already knew Apollinaire; in Paris, thanks to his friends, particularly André Breton, he discovered Alfred Jarry. Robert Desnos, his neighbor at 45, rue Blomet, was among all the Surrealists past master in diabolical play with words; his book, *Corps et biens*, is a perilous and brilliant exercise. All the Surrealists frenziedly manipulated language. They loved the word for itself— to the point of looting it of its meaning—and made use of all

possible figures of rhetoric with humor, audacity, and fury. André Breton and Philippe Soupault published their efforts at automatic writing in *Les Champs magnétiques* in 1921. Language no longer was in the exclusive service of banal communication. Instead, new words were derived and thrown off their pinnings so as to emancipate them, to give them new energy and power. Here, perhaps, is another strand of our skein: neck-breaking double and triple cartwheels, a tightrope walk that, for Miró, was a familiar game.

Most specialists interested in the relations between poetry and Miró's painting take as principal points of reference Apollinaire's *L'Enchanteur pourrissant* and *Les Mamelles de Tirésias* and Jarry's *Surmâle* and *Ubu Roi.* Besides their qualities of form and invention, they fascinated Miró precisely because they develop themes that reappear in his own work with only minor variations and with utmost constancy; thus they are no less his than theirs. Those themes form a constellation animated by many movements and attractions which, like pedestals for a *Statue* (plate 10), organize the mental space in which Miró seems to travel. In *L'Enchanteur pourrissant*, the man and woman are always separated. The woman, "twelve times impure," is sullied in flesh and soul. Man and woman are conscious of the definitive impossibility of meeting and loving. In *Les Mamelles de Tirésias*, which concerns "the grave problem of repopulation," Apollinaire gnashes his teeth and surrenders to derision rather than humor. *Surmâle* is the history of a queen (Messalina) reincarnated as a man (André Marcueil), specialist in the virile feats that arouse man's inordinate hopes, eternal and universal phantasms. *Ubu Roi* is many things, but, above all, it is an atrocious mechanism for pointing an accusing finger at the tyranny of power, whatever its stripe.

11. "*:Photo ceci est la couleur de mes rêves.*" 1925. Oil on canvas, 38 × 51" (96.5 × 129.5 cm). Collection Pierre Matisse, New York

Borrowing the title of the book by Breton and Soupault, Margit Rowell organized a major exhibition in 1972 at the Solomon R. Guggenheim Museum, New York, called "Joan Miró: Magnetic Fields." In the catalogue, she and Rosalind E. Krauss went deeply into the question of the rapport between poetry and Miró's painting, exploring the entire network (both certain and uncertain) of the encounters the painter could have had, the acquaintances acquired, and the likely influences admitted. Quite rightly, they emphasized the complex mechanism of the *calligramme*, the picture-poem that, according to Michel Foucault, "aspires playfully to efface the oldest oppositions of our alphabetical civilization; to show and to name; to shape and to say; to reproduce and to articulate; to imitate and to signify; to look and to read." Besides counterbalancing and repeating the poem's meaning, the calligramme has always used all its ingenious resources "to trap things in a double cipher."[15]

To Apollinaire we owe the revival of this very special poetic form in which the line shapes the word and vice versa: "The relationships between the juxtaposed shapes of my poems are just as expressive as the words that compose them," as he put it.[16] These "lyrical ideograms," as he called them, impose a special orientation in the reading: "The single direction is suppressed for the reader; the horizontal, vertical, zigzag, curve show themselves in turn, belonging more to the thing plastically invoked than to the conventional laws by which we read. The word is 'line and direction as much as meaning.' "[17]

Further explored in the exhibition catalogue were the kind of typographical dispositions very frequent since Cubism, in which different typefaces and bodies share the space on a page. Depending on their shape as well as the space between them, depending on the density of the ink and the extent of the white surface on which they are printed, the words take on weight, lightness, presence, and even dilate so as to become charged with a particular, allusive meaning. The plastic element converses with the sentence. The catalogue further and very lucidly examined the linguistic procedures, rhetorical figures, and tricks of language whose every cog, gear, and whim Miró understood, thanks to his friends, the poets.

A canvas like "*:Photo ceci est la couleur de mes rêves*" (1925; plate 11), if one gives exact attention to what is written on it (Photo this is the color of my dreams), is intriguing on various levels and affords a remarkable example of the theme of painting/poetry. Of all the works Miró produced in those years, this is probably one of the most stripped of plastic effects. As Rosalind Krauss put it, the great problem for Miró at the time was to define a pictorial space without resorting to description.[18] This new space is very different from that in the canvases that have been called "detailist," in which, without being illusionistic—since Miró deliberately ignored volume and weight—he nonetheless preserved the elementary geometrical structures of what we take as realistic representation. Here, in the canvas under discussion, if it were not that the words had to come in that particular place, the picture itself could be reversed. The forms would change their place without making the basic layout lose its plastic equilibrium. The word, the sentence, the spot would continue the conversation among themselves and with the blank surface. In this sense, the arrangement of the elements in this work is a sort of shape that at one and the same time holds both calligramme and typographical play. Margit Rowell proposes to read it thus: "This is a reproduction of the color of my dreams which is blue."[19] To explain the choice of that color, she refers to the very frequent use of blue in Mediterranean countries, where it is freighted with diverse and profound significances on the levels of myth, superstition, and hygiene as well. The imprecise shape and the color of the spot would be no less important, representing the basic stuff of the painter's dreams or hallucinations. Finally, she relates the picture to Mallarmé's poem "Un Coup de dés." As she sees it, the poet sets up an opposition between "the notion of *azur* or the unattainable spiritual heights, and that of the abyss—*le gouffre*—or metaphysical depths in the Baudelairean tradition."[20] Mallarmé's work was illustrated by André Masson in 1914, and Miró could have seen and read it in the studio of his friend and neighbor in rue Blomet.

Still, despite Miró's taste for difficult poets, this particular canvas seems to belong somewhat more to the arch and clever genre of "now you see it, now you don't." It precedes by one year another celebrated canvas, "*Un Oiseau poursuit une abeille et la baisse*" (A Bird pursues a bee and brings it down) of 1926 (plate 59), where the surprise comes from the mental short circuit set off between the

12. *Collage.* 1964. Watercolor and collage on paper, 29⅛ × 41⅜" (74 × 105 cm)

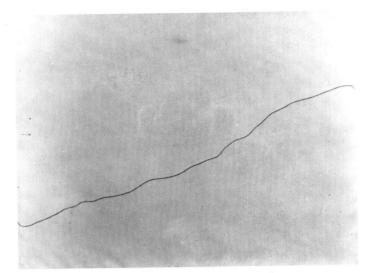

13. *Mural Painting for the Cell of a Solitary I.* 1968. Oil on canvas, 8' 10¼" × 11' 7¾" (2.7 × 3.55 m). Fundació Miró, Barcelona

words *baisser* (bring down) and *baiser* (vulgarism for the sexual act), the one with an additional letter bringing to mind the other, suggesting one and the same act. For his part, Jacques Dupin prefers to see in it no more than a simple spelling error perpetuated, arguing that the fine distinction of the *s* between two vowels would never have entered the mind of a Catalan peasant. He has in fact pointed out the persistence of this sort of inadvertence in Miró's correspondence. It is true that Miró's humor most often derives from structure, from the particular placement of forms and colors within a specific space.

On the other hand, Miró detested quibbles and thunderous pronouncements, his entire demeanor proving that he struggled against everything conventional, against society's "shoulds," against whatever smacked of respected dogma. Briefly we must note that when Surrealism came into existence Miró already had to his credit the astounding canvases turned out between 1923 and 1925, notably *The Tilled Field, Montroig* (plate 60) and *The Harlequin's Carnival* (plate 73), and had painted or was preparing to paint *Female Bather* (plate 65), *Head of Catalan Peasant* (plates 77, 79), *The Siesta* (plate 76), and others. These remarkable canvases would have their sequels in the landscapes and figures of 1926 and 1927 (plates 86–91), products of a deliberate rigor. These were not accepted without reservations by his Surrealist comrades.

When Miró painted "*:Photo,*" Surrealism was then officially one year old, and *La Révolution Surréaliste,* the movement's periodical, reproduced some of Miró's paintings. Miró's solo exhibition in Pierre Loeb's gallery, in which Miró seemed at one with the Surrealists, was a true Surrealist event, further confirmed by his participation in the Surrealists' first group exhibition in the same gallery, still in 1925. The harmony between them seemed perfect. And yet... In the first edition of *Le Surréalisme et la Peinture,* Breton finally accorded a few lines to Miró's painting, yet with a reproach plain to read: "Joan Miró cherishes perhaps one single desire—to give himself up utterly to painting, and to painting alone (which, for him involves limiting himself to the one field in which we are confident that he has substantial means at his disposal), to that pure automatism which for my part, I have never ceased to invoke, but whose profound value and significance Miró unaided has, I suspect, verified in a very summary fashion." And with due arrogance

Breton added: "With all due respect to a few idiots, I take this opportunity of affirming the indefeasibility of certain rights other than those of painting...."[21]

Jacques Dupin, Miró's most fully authorized historian, insists on the painter's quite independent attitude. Although in that period Miró was experiencing a feverish and even delirious intellectual activity, he kept his distance. Dupin puts it neatly: "He was a believer but not the kind who attends church regularly. He was not too often to be found at the Café Cyrano in the Place Blanche, where the Surrealists held their daily meetings at this time. When he did go he rarely took part in the quarrels and debates.... His famous capacity for keeping quiet in company preserved him from all the squabbles.... 'He has stayed intact,' André Masson said later."[22]

The most serious charge against him: Miró kept his independence. He adamantly refused to go in for automatism and more and more left behind the realistic, photographic reproduction of dreams. In 1936, after having praised Pierre Bonnard and Aristide Maillol (with a tinge of deliberate provocation toward the Surrealists), whose development and demanding steadfastness he admired, in speaking of the "tragic position of the artist" he commented, without naming names but with a certain aggressiveness: "Not in a well-heated *brasserie,* in any case. Not with intellectuals devoid of responsibility. *Not in the service of their absurd theories*" (emphasis added).[23] The target of this diatribe is easy to discern. All dissension begins somewhere, so that even if this cluster of quotations actually brings together a series of remarks made later, it is no less true that early on Miró and the Surrealists came to differ deeply in the way they envisaged the dream on the theoretical level and, specifically, as regards its automatic transcription. It probably took no more than some troublemaker, some irritating remark pronounced at the wrong moment and promptly evaporated in the ether around Place Blanche or between the Métro station Cambronne and the nearby rue Blomet to spark off in Miró the idea of the painted riposte of the canvas provocatively titled "*:Photo ceci est la couleur de mes rêves*" (plate 11).[24]

Whence, I think, we can hazard another meaning for that enigmatic picture. Veiled by its author's innate reserve, marked by his familiarity with verbal juggleries and his own taste in painting,

14, 15. The Fundació Joan Miró, Barcelona

its structure itself suggests a different interpretation. To begin with, the composition copies the form generally used in writing an address. In the same spirit, it can be said to be an address in the rhetorical sense of the word. And, incontestably, it is an *adresse*, an example of cleverness and skill, in its working out of a message whose meaning is open to all yet that probably remains in code. The obvious masks something else.

The word *photo* itself may contain a many-layered store of possible meanings. While a photograph is a duplicate of reality on paper, it is also the product of the automatic procedure utilized to record it. The word has five letters, and in the painting it occupies the place usually taken by the sender's name.

The large size of the letters, obviously justified on the formal plane, also attests to the importance Miró attached to the word and, at the same time, the extent to which it concerned him. Thus, the word-screen *photo* hides a very suggestive French five-letter word, probably the vulgar word *merde*, as well as Miró's own name, situated as it is where the sender's name would go on a letter. As for the sentence that gives the picture its title, it is placed where the addressee's name and address generally go. The elegance of the handwriting confers on it something of an official air, and the care with which it is written manifests, despite everything, the sender's esteem and respect for the person for whom it is destined. Further, although their displacement encumbers the writing of the superscription—which carries the key to the picture's significance— the two dots placed before the word *photo* lead one to think that they point to the end or conclusion of an address, in the rhetorical sense, as an oratorical apostrophe. The calm, measured space, white as a label or envelope, confirms the self-confident determination of the painter-writer. It is also an empty surface where no image is reflected. It is *absence*. The blue spot frayed like a postage stamp, irregular as a blob of sealing wax, affirms the solemnity of the message.

If the word *photo* so carefully positioned conceals Miró's name in order to camouflage his refusal of the Surrealists' automatism and photographic aesthetics, the conspicuousness of the full sentence likewise dissimulates its real significance. The colors white and blue, rather like the form in a calligramme, give point and shape to what is written and give rise to a different level of meaning. In operating within the context of painting itself—of his own kind of painting, which was more or less openly criticized—Miró was remaining faithful to himself. Like people who are fed up, he was addressing

a friendly but irritated *merde* to his censors, who might see there no more than a splash of blue.

Rosalind Krauss's very elaborate studies of Miró's structures, after dividing his total output into coherent groups, leave the mind on the track of connections, exchanges, and possibilities. For all the learned analysis, the purported equivalence of Miró's painting with poetry is not convincing, leaving one to wonder if in fact it exists.

In conclusion, Krauss recalled Miró's comment to Peter Watson: "Poetry, *plastically expressed*, speaks its own language" (emphasis added).[25] This proposition seems to call for examination. In his conversation of 1936 with Georges Duthuit, published as "Où allez-vous, Miró?," the painter returned to that theme at least twice: "Moreover, as you see, I attach an increasingly great importance to the subject matter of my pictures. A rich and vigorous content appears to me necessary in order to give the viewer that head-on blow which must strike him before reflection intervenes. Thus, poetry, expressed plastically, speaks its own language. . . . For a thousand men of letters, find me one poet! And I make no distinction between painting and poetry. It happens that I illustrate my pictures with poetic phrases and vice versa; didn't the Chinese, those great lords of the mind, proceed in just that way?"[26] In this context, poetry does not seem to depend on learned linguistic theories and language structures. If it did, its plastic, visual guise would be quite useless. There is much else that Miró could have said, but that one proposition of a "rich and vigorous content" appeared essential to him for pictorial poetry to have the force and intensity it attains in certain poems that he considered "real" poetry. To go with a strong poetry there must be a forceful plastic, pictorial expression that allows for a reciprocal development. Thus, in the theater in which Miró placed himself, poetry is what it has to be: perpetual revolt.

In the course of this book, the words *metaphor* and *metonymy* will often be used, for lack of equivalents applicable to the visual arts, to represent the stylistic procedures found also in painting. Much as one would like to discover a common structure for painting and poetry, the conclusion—if there is one—may have to be Kandinsky's reflection: "As they grow deeper, each art closes itself off and becomes separate."[27]

After much scholarly debate, neither poets, painters, nor literary critics have been able to decide just what was Cubist about the calligramme, to which that label had been applied rather hastily. The forms of painting and poetry do not coincide exactly. Between

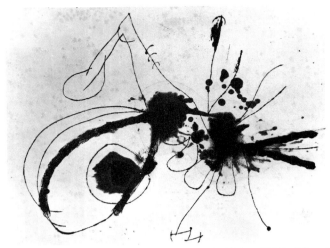

16. *Bird of Prey*. 1972. Brush and India ink, 19⅝ × 25⅝" (50 × 65 cm)

them there is always a distance, a cruel gap. Whatever a word's derivation, in a particular context it retains something of a latent sense, a dynamism, a force. The shapes of painting, however violated and whatever their avatars, remain symbolic. A word, a phrase do not replace a form, a color. Yet, in both cases, they evoke and provoke the imagination. A poem or painting worth reading or looking at is never the product of everyday routine. Both always transcend it. Poetry is an affair of words, painting of the eye. As Bachelard put it, while words perform well enough the everyday tasks we want from them, above a certain level they become open to confusion. And it is their ambiguity that gives rise to poetry. Forms, too, become ambiguous and poetical once they lose their everyday context. And, despite this parallel, the structures of poetry and painting differ.

An image, figurative or not, conveys a body of information to the eye and also possesses an impact on the plane of emotion that word and phrase do not convey in comparable manner. The absence of imagination is not a factor here. An image, in all circumstances, is a cluster of intricate messages. *Seeing* is always an initiation, however commonplace the thing seen. In art, seeing is ultimately a way of looking face to face at the sun and at death.

Miró, one should keep in mind, told Georges Duthuit: "What counts is stripping our soul bare. Painting or poetry are made like one makes love: an exchange of blood, a total embrace, with no prudence whatsoever, with no protection at all."[28]

If since the beginning of our century "reading" in whatever form has become an adventure, even a dangerous one, Miró is one of those artists who demand that the viewer too take risks (with due allowance made), no less than he himself has done through the entire journey toward awareness, in the open-hearted hope of making the viewer a true fellow traveler, a genuine interlocutor.

By taking out-of-the-way paths, often difficult because they run counter to prejudices, official principles, conventional ideas, common denominators, Miró's painting cries: *revolt*. By this, he understood fighting against all those ubiquitous individuals with hardening of the brain, those with seats in the establishment who will not grant the poet, the artist, his proper place in the world— the first place—those who respect a sole principle: profit. Through his painting, Miró aspired to free men from the fetters that a greedy society, forever suspicious of dissent, braids from velvet and steel to do its work of oppression.

Notes

[1] Examples recorded by Julien Besançon in *Journal mural, Mai 1968* (Paris: Tchou Éditions, 1968), pp. 13, 14, 146, 147.

[2] Robert Desnos, "L'Aumonyme" (1923), *Corps et biens* (1930), reprint (Paris: Poésie-Gallimard, 1968), p. 58.

[3] André Breton, *Manifestes du Surréalisme* (Paris: Idées-Gallimard, 1981), p. 28. Eng. ed.: *Manifestoes of Surrealism*, trans. Richard Seaver and Helen R. Lane (Ann Arbor: University of Michigan Press, 1969), p. 36.

[4] Herbert Marcuse, *Eros and Civilization* (Boston: Beacon Press, 1955), pp. 94–95.

[5] Ibid., p. 50.

[6] André Breton, "Le Marquis de Sade a regagné," *Clair de terre* (Paris: Gallimard, 1966), p. 165.

[7] Breton, *Manifestes du Surréalisme*, p. 50; Eng. ed., p. 18.

[8] "*Displacement*, by which a representation, often of insignificant appearance, can have attributed to it the full psychological value, significance, intensity originally attributed to something else....*Condensation*, into a single representation may flow together all the meanings carried by the associational chains which happen to intersect." J. Laplanche and J.-B. Pontalis, *Vocabulaire de la Psychanalyse* (Paris: Presses Universitaires Françaises, 1973), p. 342.

[9] André Breton, *Le Surréalisme et la peinture*, 3rd ed., rev. (Paris: Gallimard, 1965), p. 70. Eng. ed.: *Surrealism and Painting*, trans. Simon Watson Taylor (New York: Harper & Row, 1972), p. 70.

[10] Pierre Loeb, *Voyages à travers la peinture* (Paris: Bordas, 1946), p. 48.

[11] Arthur Rimbaud, *Oeuvres complètes* (Paris: Gallimard, 1946), pp. 251–58.

[12] Georges Duthuit, "Où allez-vous, Miró?," *Cahiers d'Art* (Paris) 11, nos. 8–10 (1936), pp. 257–66.

[13] Michel Foucault, *Raymond Roussel* (Paris: Gallimard, 1963), p. 55.

[14] Raymond Roussel, *Comment j'ai écrit certains de mes livres* (Paris: Librairie Alphonse Lemerre, 1935), p. 9.

[15] Michel Foucault, *Ceci n'est pas une pipe* (Paris: Gallimard, 1968), pp. 84–85. Eng. ed.: *This Is Not a Pipe*, trans. and ed. James Harkness (Berkeley: University of California Press, 1983), pp. 21, 20.

[16] Guillaume Apollinaire, "Gazette des Lettres," *Paris-Midi*, 22 July 1914.

[17] Renée Riese Hubert, "Apollinaire et Picasso," *Cahiers du Sud* 40, no. 1 (1966), p. 26.

[18] Rosalind E. Krauss and Margit Rowell, *Joan Miró: Magnetic Fields* (New York: Solomon R. Guggenheim Foundation, 1972), p. 38.

[19] Ibid., p. 60.

[20] Ibid., p. 61.

[21] Breton, *Le Surréalisme et la peinture*, pp. 37, 41; Eng. ed., pp. 36, 41.

[22] Jacques Dupin, *Joan Miró* (Paris: Flammarion, 1961), p. 148. Eng. ed.: trans. Norbert Guterman (New York: Harry N. Abrams, 1962), p. 154. This and other excerpts and citations from Dupin in the following pages are taken from this translation, with occasional minor modifications.

[23] In Duthuit, "Où allez-vous, Miró?," pp. 257–66.

[24] The stretch of Métro's line 2 between Passy and Place d'Italie (now line 6) was opened to the public in 1906. The Cambronne station has never changed its name. Information from the Service Historique de la Direction de la R.A.T.P.

[25] In Krauss and Rowell, *Joan Miró: Magnetic Fields*, p. 38.

[26] In Duthuit, "Où allez-vous, Miró?," pp. 257–66.

[27] In Claude Debon, "Cubisme et Littérature: L'Écriture Cubiste d'Apollinaire," *Europe* (Paris), June–July 1982, p. 124.

[28] In Duthuit, "Où allez-vous, Miró?," pp. 257–66.

17. *The Pedicure.* 1901. Watercolor, gouache, and pencil, 4½ × 7″ (11.6 × 17.7 cm). Fundació Miró, Barcelona

"Just as the entire body is of the same nature as an arm, a hand, a foot, everything must be homogeneous in a picture." —MIRÓ TO YVON TAILLANDIER

Artisan, craftsmanship: these words call to mind fidelity to a tradition, a pronounced taste for fine material often obtained by simple or poor means, a deep sense of individuality placed in the service of the collectivity, a clear and well-defined position within society. In surveying the entire course of Miró's work we shall see that, whatever the metamorphoses, the artist remained faithful to that attitude, to those tastes, and to that function proudly assumed. These are elements of Miró's background—his father was a well-established jeweler and watchmaker in Barcelona—that were to reappear transformed or disguised.

For Joan Miró, as for most children, it all began with drawing. The first sheets preserved date from 1901. Born in 1893, the boy was then eight. At school he was already attending the optional drawing classes taught by a Señor Civil. The first things he depicted were everyday objects, domestic animals, pots of flowers, and then a first scene from family life: the pedicure (plate 17), which makes a curious incursion into his world. To be honest, those drawings are neither clumsy nor skillful, with no signs of a precocious virtuosity. Instead, they exhibit an attentive, perhaps stubborn application. On the symbolic level, however, the only one on which they might yield an answer, they do take on meaning. A cottage: the fire is out in the hearth, no smoke escapes from the chimney, thus a house with its due burden of feeling, yet cold. Shrubs carefully laid out across the surface of the paper are neat and straight and solid. Firmly planted, flowers sink their roots into pots too big or too small for their height (plates 20, 21). A human foot introduces the subject of sex. This pampered, well-cared-for foot will later become both furrow and plowshare in *The Farmer's Wife* (1922–23; plate 56), will stand for *The Gentleman* (1924; plate 72) and one of two *Lovers* (1925; plate 81), will serve as a base for a tall *Statue* (1925; plate 10), and will end up, exasperated, launching a stone at a pesky bird (1926; plate 89). As for the bird, driven off in impatience or scorn, it would revenge itself by returning again and again, always hanging around, as in *"Un Oiseau poursuit une abeille et la baisse"* (1926; plate 18). The same bird is to be found always fluttering

around women. In innumerable canvases in Miró's oeuvre, a bird appears in some whimsical guise or on one pretext or another. Turning Georges Limbour's reflection into a question—Would it really be out of place to comment philosophically on such bits of imagination?—we can turn the question itself around: Why should it be out of place when, quite obviously, the importance attached to those imaginings is plain to see?

In 1908, the youth is already more confident. He knows how to take advantage of the grain of the paper, of traces of color. He positions his elements with more precision and ease. Naturally, he imitates Papa: trying his hand at his father's métier, he experiments with jewelry designs. Taking into account what was in the air at the time, what the style of the period suggested or encouraged, the boy's *Coiled Serpent* (plate 18) is an ornament worthy of Salomé, a knot ready to draw itself tight. The gaping jaw, ungrounded in anatomy, is armed with cruel fangs. On the other hand, the *Peacock* (plate 19) with fan unfurled could be an ornament for a grille or, better, a door knocker that Gaudí himself might use. Its feathers, shaped like the leaves of a plane tree, remain attached to the page's whiteness by a thick, exaggerated shadow.

Together with a few other sheets, these present evidence of a difficult childhood. In a remarkable series of conversations with Georges Raillard published in 1977, Miró recalled his early years: "I felt that isolation in a very painful, very drastic manner when I was very young, still a child.... With my parents there was an absolute barrier." At that late date, drawing a lesson from all the years of his life, he could permit himself to say: "And I am very glad for it.... The life I led in my childhood let me develop muscles.... The difficulties, that's what gave me muscles" (p. 18).

The human child remains dependent on its parents longer than does any other animal. His apprenticeship under them leaves definitive traces in his psychological makeup, which will repeatedly surface, metamorphosed, throughout his existence. What is severely oppressed, misunderstood, or repressed will surge forth elsewhere, transformed, probably warped. The child's fragility, his physical weakness in the face of the paternal and maternal giants, his difficulties (with which we are all familiar) give rise to anxiety. To be put at rest, such anxiety needs to be sublimated to the benefit of

18. Jewelry design: *Coiled Serpent.* 1908. Charcoal and pencil, 19⅛ × 24¾″ (48.5 × 63 cm). Fundació Miró, Barcelona

19. *Peacock.* 1908. Charcoal and chalk, 19½ × 25″ (49.5 × 63.6 cm). Fundació Miró, Barcelona

some rewarding, appreciated activity. The suppression of what the child caught sight of one day, of what he so much wanted to look at but was forbidden to see, will have a determining role in the future choice of an activity in which *seeing* becomes the sublimation of the primal scene. For the person endowed with talent and heightened sensitivity, art—painting and, even more, sculpture—remains the privileged outlet that permits unlimited repetitions, in metaphorical guises, of a first surge of emotion, a first and never-satisfied desire.

At fourteen Miró, to his sorrow, was constrained to endure schooling meant to fit him for a commercial career that was not at all to his taste. He took his revenge by enrolling in classes in La Lonja School of Fine Arts in Barcelona. Two teachers there, Modesto Urgell and José Pasco, deeply influenced him. The first confirmed for the already very reserved boy that solitude is a state infinitely superior to the dazzling tumult enjoyed by a considerable part of so-called active mankind. The second conferred on him the freedom to take what he could from an already liberal teaching and incited him to develop his natural gifts for vivid coloring. Miró would never forget the significance and efficacy of these salutary lessons, of a freedom deeply felt.

But the constraints became too heavy. A miserable year spent scratching paper as clerk in the accounting department of the Dalmau Oliveiras Company was paid for with twelve disheartening months of illness and a long convalescence in the family country house in Montroig. That year, he stopped painting: "Painting being for him a matter of concentrating his entire being, of an enthusiastic and thoughtful elaboration of things seen, a labor to occupy every last instant, it was impossible for him to paint in the rare moments when his tasks as office worker left him free" (Christian Zervos). It seems very likely that his illness was psychosomatic.

Yet it was in that small village near Tarragona that, in his own mind, the young man felt himself reborn. "The soil of Montroig: I sense it more and more, but I have been sensing it since I was a youngster.... For me it was a physical necessity. I was very isolated. No one gave a damn about me, very isolated..." (to Georges Raillard, 1977, p. 18). To Camilo José Cela he said, "One needs to paint with the earth underfoot, because force enters via the feet," and later, in 1976, to Gaëtan Picon: "I found my footing in

Montroig" (Eng. ed., p. 17). To these, Jacques Dupin, in his irreplaceable book on Miró, added: "While he keeps his feet on the ground the better to draw strength and inspiration from the earth, his eye introduces order into the teeming images and assures the right functioning of the delicate mechanisms of revelation. Feet and eyes—which themselves occupy a prominent place in Miró's vocabulary of symbols—were in his case formed in Montroig, in the landscape of Tarragona, in the smithy of Cornudella" (pp. 34–35).

Despite vehement protests following hard on insidious sermons that cast doubt on both his capabilities and the possibilities of his ever earning a living through them, Miró succeeded in getting his way. In 1912 he enrolled in the Escola d'Arte Galí. As could be expected from one already resolute in revolt, he sided with the insurgents; the school, according to Miró's friend J. F. Rafols, was "a cry of protest against the academicians of La Lonja." The painter Galí, a strong, independent personality, was a remarkable pedagogue. Before accepting a new pupil he subjected him to something we might call psychological testing: first a long conversation by which to gauge the potential recruit's character, then a technical examination designed to reveal the student's qualities, failings, predilections. Miró's determination made a good impression. The brilliance of his colors—asked to paint a still life of grayish drab objects, he produced, Miró later said, "a sunset"— amazed the teacher. Galí felt in sympathy with his new pupil, and Miró himself found in this new Socrates, for the first time in his life, support and confidence. Nor did Galí's influence stop there. He sought to open his pupils' eyes and minds: "Galí used to talk about Manet, Van Gogh, Gauguin, Cézanne, and even the Fauves and Cubists. We used to spend our breaks discussing art nineteen to the dozen. But we only saw reproductions" (to Gaëtan Picon, 1976, p. 31; p. 20). The teacher's broad-mindedness helped Miró take in his stride the difficulties ahead of him. It also helped to calm the daily anxieties of a father who turned up once a week demanding assurance and reassurance concerning his son's professional aptitudes and prospects.

If Miró was already an energetic colorist, form eluded him. He simply could not distinguish a straight line from a curve on his paper. To remedy this curious handicap, Galí taught him to draw

20. *Pot of Flowers.* 1901. Pencil, 8⅜ × 4¾″ (21.2 × 12 cm). Fundació Miró, Barcelona

21. *Pot of Flowers.* 1906. Pen, India ink, and colored pencils, 19⅝ × 12¾″ (49.7 × 32.5 cm). Fundació Miró, Barcelona

22. *The Peasant.* c. 1912–14. Oil on canvas, 25⅝ × 19⅝" (65 × 50 cm)

from memory after spending a long time feeling an object while blindfolded. Touching and seeing thus became mutual aids, each in turn helping to define the form. Rather as with a mountain climber, the sense of touch confirmed what the eye perceived. Galí's unusual method, so useful in countering this odd failing, would prove invaluable for Miró. Thirty years later, conversing with James Johnson Sweeney, the artist acknowledged the benefit and effects of that exercise, seeing in it the origin of his need to mold with his hands, his taste for sculpture that allowed him to experience "a physical sensation that I cannot get from drawing or painting" ("Joan Miró: Comment and Interview," *Partisan Review* 15, no. 2, February 1948, p. 206).

As far as I know, Miró did not keep those experimental drawings, which were probably more interesting for the tension their structure revealed than for their aesthetic effects. On the other hand, there are a few nude studies from 1915 (plate 32) not unrelated in spirit to the discipline of those exercises. In these the lines are accentuated easily, furiously, and the taut, rhythmed bodies show very marked emphases and powerful modeling. They are not unrelated to Picasso's treatment of his *Les Demoiselles d'Avignon* of 1907. The young Miró was disarticulating the bodies joint by joint and cutting them up with a billhook.

Miró's ship was taking the seas, trying its sails. The wind would buffet it from the four points, there would be many and sudden squalls, not entirely unexpected.

Quite unlike hidebound, conventional Madrid, Barcelona is an active, extremely adventurous city, whose audacities, both spiritual and material, generate a true spirit of enterprise. It is by no means a provincial city. Indeed, its sheer energy, wealth, and wide-ranging influence give it title to the true first city of Spain, Madrid remaining merely the administrative core of the country. Since the

remote times when the Phoenicians came and set up their trading posts on the western shores of the Mediterranean, Barcelona has been an open city. Its port makes it a commercial center, fostering exchanges in which a keen intelligence combines with a form of frenzy proclaimed with pride and independence. Miró saw the city as an ever-renewed spectacle, discovered with the marveling but not always respectful eyes of youth. Moreover, he found there in those years a genuine intellectual effervescence and a broad spectrum of art, including the opportunity to see and study works by Impressionists, Fauves, and Cubists. In the very midst of World War I, in 1916, the great art dealer Ambroise Vollard exhibited there an important ensemble of paintings by the Parisian artists: "Vollard had made the selection. There were Manets, Monets, and even some of the earliest Matisses. It was a real eye-opener!... The greatest revelation was a Monet painting: simply a sunset" (to Gaëtan Picon, 1976, p. 33; p. 20).

Miró loved color for itself, for the pleasures it provokes. Treated with broad brushstrokes, *Peasant* (c. 1912–14; plate 22) is a somber mass with imprecise contours, poorly defined within a tangle of red, blue, and yellow touches. Those colored slashes disguise an unavowed emergence of line, where one can read the young artist's legitimate hesitations about his own means and perhaps, more simply, his current incapacity to discern his direction.

That same tension, between the line and the form it is meant to define, both enlivened and jarred in the works soon to follow. It took shape as a struggle between line and color, their interdependence or independence, the supremacy that had to be granted one or the other in order to forestall a final disappointment. The object was above all to advance toward the picture's conceptual goal, even if in that period of trial and error the result remained uncertain and the satisfaction dubious.

23. *The Coffeepot.* 1915. Oil on cardboard, 19⅝ × 21⅝″ (50 × 55 cm)

24. *Still Life with Knife.* 1916. Oil on cardboard, 23¼ × 27⅜″ (59 × 69.5 cm)

25. PAUL CÉZANNE: *Still Life with Apples and Oranges*. 1895–1900. Oil on canvas, 28¾ × 36⅝" (73 × 93 cm). Musée d'Orsay, Paris

26. HENRI MATISSE: *Red Room (Harmony in Red)*. 1908. Oil on canvas, 70⅞ × 86⅝" (180 × 220 cm). The Hermitage, Leningrad

The Coffeepot, Still Life with Knife, Still Life with Rose, "Nord-Sud"

Among *The Coffeepot* (plate 23), *Still Life with Knife* (plate 24), and *Still Life with Rose* (plate 28), one can observe changes at work and a growing mastery. As the formats become larger, self-assurance increases from canvas to canvas. Space, at first smotheringly dense, is eased and lightened. Where objects crowded each other in Miró's earliest efforts, in *Still Life with Knife* of 1916 the knife is so disposed on the table as to underline a diagonal composed of three linked elements—circle, oval, square—wedged in by the fruits to either side. Miró's composition, heretofore compressed, remains stiff, even academic. But it is the expression that is important to him here. The accentuation of the reflections emphasizes this, and the liberal use of impasto, the broad brushwork, and the frank modeling confirm it. Everything has a weight, adheres to the plane where the objects are disposed, and they have a nice, earthy heaviness.

In *Still Life with Rose*, the flower is a red spot balancing the brightness of a tomato in the hollow of a rustic bowl. The broken stripes made by the rumpled folds in the Majorcan tablecloth create an agitated zone, and this is juxtaposed and fused with the upper part of the picture, which is deliberately kept calmer. Achieving equilibrium by a calculated dosage is a difficult problem that has been felicitously overcome. A diagonal and a vertical, the bottle and its shadow, link the two planes and, further, divide the surface of the upper zone into two unequal empty spaces, which are enlivened by broken lines. While playing the role of connecting link, they nonetheless do not distract from the importance of the tabletop. The colors—browns, reds, blues—do not yet make shapes but are distributed within boundaries. They are surrounded by strong brush lines, which introduce themselves everywhere at every opportunity. The choice of these few objects and of cloths deliberately rumpled in the interest of an agitated line tell us where the artist's attention was directed: toward expressivity.

The information that reached Miró from Paris was necessarily fragmentary, but he had seen a few pictures and reproductions of

Cézanne (plate 25), who greatly impressed him. One wonders if by chance he had seen Matisse's *Red Carpet* (1906) or *Red Room (Harmony in Red)* (1908; plate 26). In any case, he succeeded in resolving the decorative problem posed by loading and overloading with ornament. It was these still lifes that he decided to show to Josep Dalmau, the most important art dealer in the city who was interested in the work of the Cubists and young artists. Happily, in view of the young artist's proud and unsociable timidity, Miró received encouragement from Dalmau.

A hard worker, obstinate and taciturn, Miró now took to frequenting life classes: "We used to choose a pose for each week. This was at the Sant Lluch school, where I went until 1918.... During our life sessions, we used to notice an old man sitting and sketching with us. It was Gaudí. We knew he was a great man. I've said that I would class Antoni Gaudí among the very greatest architects.... But I often sketched elsewhere, particularly at the Molino, a well-known Café Concert in Barcelona. It's still there. Like Toulouse-Lautrec, I enjoyed studying the women dancing and singing!" (to Gaëtan Picon, *Carnets catalans*, 1976, pp. 28–30; pp. 18–20).

From 1915 he had a studio, which for reasons of economy he shared with Ricart, a friend met at Galí's. He also worked in Montroig, where he found himself closer to his own deep roots, to the earth. For a time he neglected the strict exercise of the still life and returned to landscapes. The natural setting around his village became the object of new and impassioned explorations.

Cornudella was one of his favorite sites, and at La Roca was the hermitage of Sant Ramón, where he was always happy to return and to accompany friends. Immense purplish red rocks of porous earth, eroded by wind and rain into the most startling shapes, rise up above a plain rustling with olive and almond trees where peasants scratch the hard earth to grow their vines. The sea sparkles in the far distance. Reus, a small foothill town in the neighborhood, was the birthplace of Gaudí, architect of the fantastic. According to Miró, without Gaudí's work he himself would not be what he was. For both artists, their fertility of imagination and freeness, perhaps to excess, that they deployed within planned compositions were influenced by this prodigious landscape. For both, the hallucinatory belonged to the realm of the normal and, even more, of the natural.

But the young Miró was not yet at that point. During this formative period, he did not always know what he wanted, although he was perfectly aware of what he did not want: he rejected the decorous style taught at La Lonja. At Dalmau's and in the magazines he had discovered Cubism, the newest arrival on the art scene. Although far from captivated by it, he found its attraction strong simply because Picasso and Juan Gris, two fellow Iberians—men of his own country!—were directly involved in it. And everything Catalan counted, nothing done by a Catalan (even if he was an adopted son) could be alien to Miró.

The drawing *Seated Female Nude* (1915; plate 32) is still bound up with past experiments. *Seated Female Nude* of 1917 (plate 31), which he probably made use of in 1918 for *Nude with Mirror* (plate 46), shows what he had by then taken from Cubism and his progress in pinning down forms. He has distanced himself from the model, tamed his wildness, and held emotion in check through the force of analysis. The rough drawings in his sketchbooks from the Sant Lluch sessions show him now observing the model with a cool, lucid eye. One tentative followed hard on another, encouraged by his curiosity, and he was bringing into play all the facets of his personality all at once: optical angles are not always successive, as rational minds too often assume.

If within a general context, Miró's painting of this time seems audacious, it was actually less bold than it appeared. Without forgetting Cézanne, whose model he had for the moment put aside, he was looking above all to Van Gogh, Matisse, and the Fauves, all of whom were still poorly understood and above all barely accepted. He was carried away by his fortunate disposition toward color, by the strength of his emotions, even more by his need for intense expression. Small wonder that he was particularly attracted by Van Gogh, a man of the North who put under control his tendency to runaway color.

Not surprisingly, despair and derision often go hand in hand. In 1917 Miró counted among his friends men of biting humor. His meeting and subsequent relations with Francis Picabia, a brilliant iconoclast, probably aided the young artist to sharpen his own wit. Picabia was taking advantage of his sojourn in Barcelona to publish his poems, *Cinquante-deux miroirs*, and four issues of his pre-Dada review *391*. He had come directly from New York, and everything mechanical excited him: *The Fiancé* (1916–17) is a plain, toothed wheel, *Novia* (1917) takes on the ironical appearance of something like a bicycle or motorcycle. The high-voltage personality of an exceptional character like Picabia, who was in touch with all the noteworthy artists in revolt in France and the United States, certainly was not disagreeable to the caustic verve of Miró, who was likewise an avid reader of the new poets. In his conversations with Georges Raillard (1977), Miró said, "In 1917 Picabia and the others shook me up because they refused to bottle themselves up in purely formal problems but treated them ironically" (p. 19).

At Dalmau's—"a madman of genius, both an exploiter of artists and a benefactor to them," said Miró (in Dupin, p. 64)—he met Maurice Raynal, another Cubist poet. Max Jacob and Marie Laurencin came for awhile and settled on the Costa Brava. Miró plunged into reading Apollinaire, Blaise Cendrars, Reverdy, and others, and paid homage to them by incorporating into a still life the name of their review, *Nord-Sud* (plate 27). In that same year, 1917, Picasso passed through Barcelona in January and again in July, when a banquet was arranged in his honor. He and Miró, however, did not meet. Miró was for a time both attracted to Cubism and repelled by it by all the speculations and intellectual quibbles surrounding it. As a group movement, Cubism had come to an end with the war of 1914–18. It could not hold on after its members were dispersed, and, in any case, everything essential had been said and its artists had decamped. We cannot be sure which of their pictures Miró had seen or which reviews he had read. The theoretical battle was still going on, but in those years the critical method lacked rigor, and it was too soon for serious studies on the bases and origins of Cubism. Thus, it is hard to say what lessons Miró drew from the din of information then obtaining.

A harmony subtends the Cubist vision. Its forms are subjected to a noble and distinguished cadence, which did not interest Miró. Equilibrium did not tempt him, its yoke too tight for him. His deepest nature was drawn instead to the impossible marriage of opposites. To his quest he brought a courageous tenacity that was commensurate with the violence of his refusal. He seemed to be plagued by other demons as well, and he preferred their provocation, smothered laughter, taunts. To hear them better, he lucidly and methodically set about inventing another discipline for himself. Probably he feared himself and often others as well. If in those youthful years his body may have been demanding but inhibited, his mind was clear: "I believe that after the grandiose achievements of the French Impressionist movement—a canticle to life and optimism—after the Post-Impressionist movement, the courageous Symbolists, the synthetism of the Fauves, and the dissections of the Cubists and the Futurists, after all that we will have a free art, all interest in which will focus on the vibration of the creative spirit. These modern analytical movements will ultimately carry the spirit into the light of freedom" (from a letter to Ricart quoted in Dupin, p. 81). He could scarcely have seen or better predicted the road that lay before him.

27. *"Nord-Sud."* 1917. Oil on canvas, 24⅛ × 27⅝" (62 × 70 cm)

28. *Still Life with Rose*. 1916. Oil on cardboard, 30¼ × 29⅛" (77 × 74 cm)

29. Poster design for the periodical *L'Instant* (Barcelona). 1919. 42⅛ × 29⅞" (107 × 76 cm). Collection Joaquim Gomis, Barcelona

30. *Nude*. 1917. Pencil, 8⅜ × 6" (21.2 × 15.2 cm). Fundació Miró, Barcelona

31. *Seated Female Nude*. 1917. Pencil, 12⅜ × 8½" (31.3 × 21.5 cm). Fundació Miró, Barcelona

32. *Seated Female Nude.* 1915. Brush, India ink, watercolor, gouache, and charcoal, 24¾ × 18¾" (62.8 × 47.5 cm). Fundació Miró, Barcelona

Still, every solid construction requires foundations. If Miró, deep within himself, felt ready to apply himself to the work he had set for himself, he had a long way to go. Dalmau offered him the opportunity of an exhibition (16 February–3 March 1918), and it was virtually a retrospective, with sixty-four canvases and many drawings done between 1914 and 1917. Any public showing is always a difficult moment for an artist: he exhibits himself naked, leaves himself vulnerable. Miró approached the experience calmly and with self-confidence. He knew what he thought of his work, and that was what mattered. In a letter to Ricart, he confided, "Before I left Montroig I spread out in front of me every canvas [fourteen] I did this summer. I think they are interesting, but all the same they do seem incomplete to me" (in Dupin, p. 81).

Standing Nude

Standing Nude (plate 33) brazenly unites geometrical forms and floral ornaments, perhaps in reminiscence of some boldly decorative canvas by Matisse. So successfully are the motifs of the carpet and drape interlinked that the junction between the vertical and horizontal planes is not readily perceptible, although it appears clearly in the triangle in the right-hand side of the picture. Yet even there the painter plays it down by inserting a green plant of stylized design and tries to retract it further by giving the illusion that the drapery is not attached to the wall. Combining a pinkish

purplish red with yellow and red flowers strewn about in arabesques, he contrives a bold color relationship that almost sets one's teeth on edge and lends a disturbing accent to an already jarring picture. A violently expressive light catches on the razor-sharp edges of the volumes. The hard, polished forms dovetail with a mechanical precision, their separate parts disposed in orderly fashion. The brilliance of the colors serves to distract the attention from the artist's crushing contempt for this iron-hard, crooked body of a young woman, become the vehicle of an artist's phantasms. If Miró had not yet fully renounced Cubism, he felt himself cramped by that maieutic of form, by that new interrogation of pictorial space. He was himself too tightly wound, too tumultuous to be able to grow while tied down to an austere rule so obsessed with organization.

The Balcony, Baja San Pedro

The Balcony, Baja San Pedro (plate 34), *Standing Nude* (plate 33), and *Still Life with Coffee Mill* (plate 35) derive above all from Cézanne's advice to "see in nature the cylinder, sphere, and cone" and the remark, "Nature is more depth than surface." To eliminate the traditional tricks of perspective and to respect the plane of the canvas without trickery, Miró was led, in order to suggest a third dimension, to interlock his forms and establish his planes in a shallow space (*The Balcony, Standing Nude*) or to stagger the planes

33. *Standing Nude.* 1918. Oil on canvas, 59⅞ × 48″ (152 × 122 cm). The Saint Louis Art Museum, Mo. Friends Fund

34. *The Balcony, Baja San Pedro.* 1917. Oil on canvas, 15¾ × 13¾″
(40 × 35 cm)

35. *Still Life with Coffee Mill.* 1918. Oil on canvas, 24⅝ × 27¾″
(62.5 × 70.5 cm)

(Still Life with Coffee Mill). In *The Balcony*, the formula is still
tentative. The foremost plane impels the eye toward the rear, but
suddenly everything becomes closer, tighter, rising up like a
veritable wall. In accord with the Cubist modalities, it shows what
perspective would have concealed, namely the thickness of the
rolled-up screen above the window. A graphic and decorative motif
is extracted from the undulation of the Roman tiles at the roof's
edge. The only curve in the picture, this takes on considerable
importance and conveys a real visual pleasure. Ultimately, the
picture brings to mind a painted stage drop.

Still Life with Coffee Mill

In *Still Life with Coffee Mill* (plate 35), which, as Dupin has
remarked, is probably the most Cubist of all his works, Miró was
more positive in his choices and decisions. The objects were chosen
primarily for their geometrical forms, the perspective is frankly
heightened, and each shift in plane is underscored by a
transformation in color. The pictorial ground is itself treated like
wallpaper with angular motifs. The lines of color hemming the
table, like the reflections enlivening the objects, have a decorative
value obviously much to Miró's taste. He contrives a harmonious
effect for the handle of the grinder by giving it a parallel in the
curve of the pipestem. And then, having seen Cubist collages, he
dutifully introduces a business card, and its machine-made
alienness to all the rest makes for an energetic intrusion of crude
reality. Whether it is considered a note of deliberate awkwardness
or of supreme skill, the commercial intruder is not absorbed into
the whole but seems to float above the table, and thereby doubly
imposes itself on our eye. The opposition is flagrant, and the

encounter between paint and print creates a disconcerting though
salubrious shock. Chromatically, the whole lies within a register of
muted earth colors.

Portraits

The series of portraits (plates 36–38) done one after the other, like
all the works from 1917 or early 1918, are marked by a search for
expressiveness. Miró, however, was incapable of copying. He could
not take over another painter's style without transforming it,
bending it to his own needs or, even more, his current capacities.
Going against the styles he admired at that time, he remained
prudent in color range and technical execution, less inclined to
feverish excess. Even when he aimed for synthesis, his eye
continued to focus on smaller factors, laying out planes that create
structure as well as the impression of forms in flux (plate 36). Still
lacking the courage for an outright yellow or red, he felt he had to
blend them, although he used complementary colors with some
pertinence (plate 37). He had not yet shaken off his art-school
lessons and was still too close to the Impressionists. In its twists and
turns, his line camouflaged a certain humor, perhaps even derision.
The motif of black-and-white stripes becomes hallucinatory
through repetition (plate 38). His eye was sharp, harsh. The
portraits seem very Russian—a strange relationship, but writers on
music have noticed common assonances, a remote and bizarre
spiritual connection, between Russian and Iberian musicians of the
late nineteenth century. Were it not for the *porron*, the flask that
points to V. Nubiola's nationality, this could be the portrait of an
agronomic engineer with his elbow resting on the rickety table in
some gaudily painted Ukrainian inn.

36. *Portrait of V. Nubiola.* 1917. Oil on canvas, 41 × 44½″ (104 × 113 cm). Folkwang Museum, Essen

37. *Portrait of Heriberto Casany (The Chauffeur).* 1918. Oil on canvas, 27⅝ × 24⅜″ (70 × 62 cm). Collection Mr. Edward A. Bragaline, New York

38. *Portrait of Juanita Obrador.* 1918. Oil on canvas, 27⅝ × 24⅜″ (70 × 62 cm). Art Institute of Chicago. Joseph Winterbotham Collection

"Certainly a picture cannot satisfy me right away.... There is a constant struggle between me and what I am doing, between me and the canvas, between me and my malaise. That struggle excites me and stirs my enthusiasm. I work until the malaise lets up." —TO YVON TAILLANDIER

Painters will tell you that an exhibition marks a pause in their progress. Seen in an outside setting, their own pictures become more or less strange, removed. After the break in concentration, the threads have to be picked up and tied again. The operation is often delicate, almost always difficult. Not the least problem is dealing with the criticisms (which, like effusive praise, often ring false) and misinterpretations elicited by the exhibition. The agitation that inevitably accompanies an exhibition is succeeded by an imprecise state in which confusion and questions bounce off one another. The artist thinks he knows what he has done but does not know how he will start up again. A blankness, a void stretches before him, and he must bridge it by making a first move. This moment of hesitation, which may drag on, is painful, often endured with impatience, irritation, or discouragement.

Action is the only possible escape, as the artist knows, yet it takes time to put his scattered forces back together. Sometimes the gears go into mesh again simply by doing routine chores in the studio: rearranging things, washing neglected brushes, preparing the canvases, with their terrifying white blankness, opening the windows and airing out the place, straightening up. Such stubborn application is another way of ordering one's thoughts so as to see more clearly and find one's way again.

As his first decision, Miró chose Montroig over Barcelona. Close to the earth, he could reflect, regroup his forces, quiet the internal uproar in order to hear his own voice again, for which he needed silence. Between the earth and himself, communication takes root more rapidly, the juices flow again: "I feel like a plant," he would tell Georges Raillard (1977).

Nothing can tell us more about his state at the time than these lines from a letter written to his friend Rafols in August of that year, 1918. Even the rhythm of the sentences is revealing. It flows without disturbances, limpidly, as if mind and heart had suddenly discovered serenity: "When I set to work on a landscape, the first thing I do is to love it, with a love born of slow understanding— slow understanding of its great richness of nuances, the concentrated richness that the sun endows it with. What happiness to manage to comprehend a single blade of grass in the landscape—why scorn a blade of grass?—that blade of grass is as beautiful as any tree or mountain. Except for the primitives and the Japanese, nobody has ever taken a good look at this thing which is so divine. Artists are always looking for great masses of trees or mountains to paint, never attuning their ears to the music that emanates from tiny flowers, blades of grass, and little pebbles in a gully" (in Dupin, p. 83). To learn from another letter that he likens himself to Saint Francis of Assisi confirms what the text makes clear: that the young artist, exhausted by his first public showing, in one way or another had great need of love. Unable to satisfy that desire, for a reason he alone could know, he was projecting onto all of nature the tenderness he himself longed for. He directs his fervor of feeling—not his passion—toward everything frail, small, forgotten, and disdained by men, and turns against the attention others bring to what is great, strong, impressive to the eye, against their "great masses of trees or mountains."

Thus he found himself in the grip of a profound nostalgia, a heartfelt regret, as if he had need of being, himself, minute enough to creep into the hollow, the breast, of nature. (This is an observation to be kept in mind, because already Miró perceived no hierarchy between the diverse elements that make up nature; affectively, each thing held the same importance and merited equal interest.) Behind appearances, behind his public face, Miró apparently found his recent experience painful. He was seeking a refuge that, unfortunately, he would not find. Work was his only resource. To his marveling eyes, the world he engaged with suddenly seemed different. To decipher it, he would soon invent for himself a new handwriting.

Having founded the "Agrupacio Courbet" with Ricart, Artigas, and other young artists of the Sant Lluch circle, he exhibited with his comrades his "detailist" canvases of 1918 and then—at last— made a great decision: he suddenly set a date for a trip to Paris. Journeys often have an ambiguous significance. They may mean a total break and the need for renewal, but they also offer the opportunity of opening one's eyes on something different in order to close them against something that has become insupportable, an excuse to stop looking at it. Miró summed up his situation in a letter to Ricart (in Dupin, p. 90):

A. I am 26 years old.

B. Of the little money I earned from my job and banked, something between 25 and 30 pesetas is left. I used the rest to buy paints and pay the studio rent. Recently, watching my little fortune dwindle, I have much against my will asked my mother for a few duros.

C. Nevertheless—confidentially—I know that when I leave home and go to Paris I can count on a small sum that will let me live and work for a while.

D. If I stay in Barcelona, I see no way out but to take the first stupid thing that comes along to earn enough money to paint.

39. *Montroig, the Village and Church.* 1919. Oil on canvas, 28¾ × 24″ (73 × 61 cm). Collection Dolorès Miró de Punyet, Palma de Majorca

40. *The House with the Palm Tree.* 1918. Oil on canvas, 25⅝ × 28¾"
(65 × 73 cm). Collection Vera Espirito Santo Saldanha, Estoril, Portugal

41. *The Trail.* 1918. Oil on canvas, 29½ × 29½" (75 × 75 cm).
Private collection, New York

The House with the Palm Tree,
The Vegetable Garden with Donkey,
The Trail

At Montroig, Miró lived quietly, keeping a close eye on the
landscape. Attracted by the closed world of the garden, he
cultivated his painting like the gardener his flower beds, with equal
care and stubborn patience. Visibly enchanted by the lines of
furrows, by newly planted seedlings, by shrubs loaded with flowers
or fruit, he found happiness in reconstituting them on canvas
without distorting their forms. Any transformation would be felt as
lack of respect; in his current state of mind, any discordance would
be wounding. Thus, everything is harmonious: the balancing of
curves, the succession of horizontals, the disposition of verticals.

From canvas to canvas the composition grows suppler. *The House
with the Palm Tree* (plate 40)—if we are correct about the order in
which this group was painted—is still stiff. He emphasizes the play
of horizontals. In the next two compositions, he was led to break
up the parallels in order to lighten them. He accomplished this in
The Vegetable Garden (plate 42) by diversifying the rectangles of the
plant beds and in *The Trail* (plate 41) by echoing the elongated
undulation of the furrows in the high cascade of the foliage. The
skies in all three paintings are traversed by clouds in rolled-up
shapes moving in a lulling rhythm. The solidity of the basic plan,
clear in all three paintings, permits the artist to accumulate a
multitude of delicate or robust detail without apparent
laboriousness or heaviness.

And for all the pains Miró takes over details, the precision does
not detract from the general aspect. Our eye, like his, delights in
his reconstitution, executed with unmistakable gentleness and
shown under a fine, strong light, of this solitary stretch of land;
this silent house beneath a blue sky of an extreme purity; this
peaceful garden where, after the hot noon hours, a quiet and
docile donkey respects its master's flower and vegetable beds and

makes do with grazing bitter weedy thistles. As Christian Zervos
remarked, Miró made "the world of things relive in his own
personal world" (*Cahiers d'Art* 9, nos. 1–4, 1934, p. 13).

These three canvases irresistibly bring to mind not the Japanese
prints in vogue since the Impressionists but the thousand-flowered
Gothic tapestries and, equally, Indian or Persian miniatures. Such
works, in their seeming simplicity, are able to join to the present
both a delicacy and a great skill in rendering space and
architecture. In them, as in these works of Miró, flowers push
through the meadow carpet, the complexity of porticoes breaks up
the perspective, a forgotten fruit dangles from the end of a branch
between two leaves gnawed by caterpillars. But where the Eastern
miniatures conjure up the games and revels of sumptuously attired
maidens and princes, Miró banishes all representation of human
beings from these canvases. Is the donkey—a humble beast,
disdained, often maltreated—perhaps meant as a symbol? Here,
only nature exists for Miró: a solitary palm tree with branches
symmetrical as a fountain, a garden without gardener, the deep
gash of the trail. In the latter painting, from the viewing point
chosen by the painter, the trees are in the distance and cast no
shade. In other pictures, the cast shadows result from the shifting
planes of the architecture and are purely arbitrary. In the final
analysis, all the artist's soft-hearted efforts and illusions do not
succeed in concealing his hard-eyed view.

On 3 March 1919, Miró arrived at the Gare d'Austerlitz, in a
Paris still teeming with horse-drawn omnibuses. For a year now,
France had been at peace. Miró would remain there until June.
Under the guidance of Artigas, whom he rejoined there, he settled
in the Hôtel de Rouen, rue Notre-Dame-des-Victoires, much
frequented by young Catalans seeking emancipation in the City of

42. *The Vegetable Garden with Donkey.* 1918. Oil on canvas, 25¼ × 27⅝″ (64 × 70 cm). Moderna Museet, Stockholm

43. *Self-Portrait.* 1919. Oil on canvas, 28¾ × 23⅝" (73 × 60 cm). Musée du Louvre, Paris. Picasso Donation

Light. Almost immediately he looked up Picasso, not so much to hand on the little packages mothers are forever consigning to travelers but to meet the painter of the thousand fireworks whose celebrity had spread well beyond the frontiers. Despite their very different characters, the two men would become and remain friends for a few decades.

Miró spent the months in Paris devoured by curiosity, swept along in a frenzied round of new encounters. Everything had to be visited: galleries, exhibitions, ateliers, and, above all, the Louvre, where the young artist spent hours every morning in deep concentration, absorbing everything he could from his first acquaintance with a major museum.

"I came to Paris with the idea of working in one of those famous academies like the Grande Chaumière, but an extraordinary thing happened to me: scarcely arrived in Paris, my hands became paralyzed. Impossible to hold a pencil in my fingers. It was not a physical paralysis but an intellectual one, the shock of Paris had been too great, and I remained for a long time unable to do anything" (to Georges Raillard, 1977, pp. 66–67).

Self-Portraits, 1917 and 1919

The self-portraits of 1917 and 1919 are diametrically opposite. The first (plate 44) is heavy, thick, uncouth, constructed from blobs of color. The second (plate 43) is icy. Treated in large planes, stylized, it tends toward purification. The face is set against a delicate golden background. The drawing is precise, the forms are clearly defined and enclosed within a network of fine steel wires that set the color into blocks. The tension is such that despite shadings and subtle transitions, the volumes are flattened. The protuberance of

the nose is skillfully—or naively—managed, without revealing the means of accomplishment.

Over this inexpressive but extraordinarily firmly laid-out face—the contours of the mouth, ridges of the brows, and parentheses of the cheeks—lies a mask, that of a translucid absence. The color is exquisite: pink for the cheekbones, blue for the globe of the eye and the freshly shaved cheeks. In the hair, drawn with delectation, strand by strand, it becomes iridescent. The pedestal of the neck supports the oval of the head, balanced by the wide opening of the red jacket with its tiny geometrical patterns. Too big, the jacket falls into woolly folds, and the attentive artist traces their scaffolding with evident satisfaction. Bluish black piping divides the garment severely into two almost equal parts, like a knife cutting a fruit, severing also the agitation of the angles underscored by shadow.

Miró's deliberate effort to exploit the accidents of relief, to reduce space, owes very little to Cubism. It seems to reveal quite a different spirit. Even if he had not yet visited the Prado, he had seen reproductions of the German, Flemish, and Dutch primitives and early works of the Spanish school. The institutions in Barcelona are rich in paintings and altarpieces of that period, and the fifteenth-century Jaime Huguet is the pride of Catalonia. Already at the age of eight, Joan went by himself to the museum in Barcelona on Sunday mornings. His eye noted how those early painters so admirably turned to account the effects that could be drawn from draperies, folds, brocades, watered silks. They knew how to make use of broken-up shapes, often as a kind of independent device within the general structure of a painting. The painted altar cloths, surplices, dalmatics preserve even the traces of long storage on shelves and in armoires and coffers. With those

44. *Self-Portrait.* 1917. Oil on canvas, 24 × 19⅝" (61 × 50 cm). Private collection, New York

45. *Portrait of a Little Girl.* 1918. Oil on paper,
13 × 11″ (33 × 28 cm). Fundació Miró, Barcelona

Portrait of a Little Girl

early painters one still finds gold grounds and polished shapes reduced to abstractions inscribed without volume on the surface of a fresco or panel. Ornamental fringes and borders were exploited to break up the surface. Miró, never at ease in the Cubist domain, turned a fresh eye to this ostensibly realistic painting, reinterpreting it in terms of his own sensibility and realizing parallels and similarities justified by a common way of understanding space, form, and color. From these painters, he would draw many additional lessons.

At the same time Miró, already a great reader of poets, gorged himself insatiably with poetry, by preference with whatever boldly attacked conventions and customs. He could not have chosen a better time than March 1919 to be in Paris. In that month, the review *Littérature* brought out its first number, under the joint editorship of Aragon, Breton, and Soupault. On 4 April 1919, after publishing this first issue, whose contents yet reflected divergent tendencies, Breton wrote to Tzara: "Killing art is what seems most urgent to me."

In conversations in 1952, Breton made it clear that "it was only the arrival of [the review] *Dada III* in Paris at the start of 1919 that set fire to our powder. Tzara's 1918 Dada manifesto, which sparked it off, was violently explosive. It proclaimed the break with art, with logic, with the necessity of 'a great negative work to be accomplished,' it praised spontaneity to the skies. For me, what counts more than what is said is what is released, at once excessive and nervous, provocative and remote, and poetic as well" (in Gaëtan Picon, *Le Journal du Surréalisme*, 1976, p. 19).

Miró was in Paris, present at the birth of what in a few years would become the tumultuous Surrealist movement.

In *Portrait of a Little Girl* (plate 45), Miró stretched line to the point of stylization, purified his form, laid out his yellows and blues in broad areas of carefully applied paint. The cat-eyed face—glacial to the point of absence—is a veritable abstraction. The colored planes, curving lines, and diagonals adjust to each other and together create a precious mechanism fabricated from fine metal: struck, it would give off a dry and crystalline tone. But this portrait, innocent in appearance, was a trap for Miró, who, as a man of the soil, perceived the danger. To evade it would require a change of mental state, and he was not yet ready for that; his need for order and tidiness had not yet run its course.

It is close to the truth to say that the crisis Miró was going through, far from fading, was gaining in intensity. He had to find another solution. His need to organize the most diverse things brings to mind those unsatisfied housewives who, to put a damper on their inner vexations, drive themselves to rub down, scour, polish, dust every object around them, and assign to each its exact place on a lace doily. The breaking point was drawing near.

Nude with Mirror

In *Nude with Mirror* (plate 46), Miró created an enigmatic picture without resorting to the techniques that generally generate an air of mystery. The positioning of every element seems to be justified exclusively on the formal plane, each drawing its efficacy from its exact situation on the surface. Little by little, one discovers that this faceted body, worked over and corrected, has insidiously

46. *Nude with Mirror.* 1918. Oil on canvas, 44⅛ × 40⅛″ (112 × 102 cm). Kunstsammlung Nordrhein-Westfalen, Düsseldorf

47. *Vines and Olive Trees, Montroig.* 1919. Oil on canvas, 28⅜ × 35⅜″ (72 × 90 cm). Collection Mr. and Mrs. Leigh B. Block, Chicago

Vines and Olive Trees, Montroig

become a highly furbished armor, that the impeccable coiffure has turned into a lacquered helmet. The delicate face is sealed in its solitude or escapes into absence. We will never know what is reflected in the mirror held out into the void. The red and blue stripes of the carpet, the fringes of the taboret with their succession of yellow ocher, red ocher, and deep ocher become an obsessional motif in their repetition and system. This naked woman, invented under the brush's caress, is mythically inaccessible.

It is probably reasonable in terms of painting to refer all this to the long realist tradition of Spanish painting. But Miró's realism seems to be more than an attempt to describe the world objectively. He brings to it something else. The repetition, the insistence, the almost disturbing care he manifests lead him to reveal other realms, other relationships with the visible. Appearances are not to be trusted; they forever conceal still others. However keenly biting the look Miró directs on what surrounds him, he looks only at himself. In this mirror one might well think blank, who is reflected? Undoubtedly Miró—and how cruel he must have found this disappointed desire to pierce the space behind the mirror.

"This Paris has shaken me up from head to foot—in the good sense," Miró writes to Rafols (in Dupin, p. 91). His eyes primed, he does not hesitate to return to work, the best way to sort out and test a multitude of new and disordered impressions.

Back home, Miró entered a new, aggressive phase, in which he dared to record in paint what nature meant to him, and rendered it with unaccustomed boldness. Across the foreground of this canvas (plate 47) he laid out horizontals at intervals, yellow furrows strewn with drooping plants, and conceived nature in terms of rectangles and broken shapes. To chime with the clatter of sharp-cut angles and hard-edged triangles, his color contrasts became violent, ranging between scorching reds and acid greens. This new landscape is a compromise, perhaps even a dry and deliberate contradiction, between the ornamental approach practiced before his journey and a geometrizing construction derived from Cubism but given new life and sharpened by what he had seen in Paris.

Dense and taut, this picture announces that dry and precise way of seeing particular to Miró. The landscape he shows us is already laid out on a grid plan. Earth, vines, trees are forms obeying another law, another will. One feels that Miró is not out to reproduce anything. Here landscape begins to become for him the subject of a provocative, independent reflection. The first link in a long chain, this canvas marked the beginning of a sharpened way of seeing that led Miró to compose without chiaroscuro, shading, and the lines and devices of perspective. It is an ambiguous and contradictory picture, hence a very rich one. Any hesitations or emotional scruples are hidden away in the remotest picture plane, where they balance the visual harshness of the two foremost planes.

48. *Horse, Pipe, and Red Flower.* 1920. Oil on canvas, 32½ × 29½" (82.5 × 75 cm). Private collection, United States

"In any case, I have to have a point of departure, even if only a grain of dust or a burst of light. That form procreates a series of things, one thing giving rise to some other thing."—TO YVON TAILLANDIER

Now Miró had a single thought: to return to Paris, to live and work there. The first visit had been a way of sniffing the air of the great city, of making contact, of measuring himself against it. The leap would be less difficult since it would not be into the unknown. He made his arrangements. Although he was ready to make sacrifices, he remained level-headed: he ceded all his pictures to Dalmau for a thousand pesetas on condition that the dealer organize a show for him in Paris. As he wrote to Ricart, "The real reason is I want to be independent of my family as soon as I can; it is distasteful to me to go on living on their handouts. This will give me enough for the fare and for two months in Paris; after that, I'll manage somehow" (in Dupin, p. 96).

All the difficulties that could block the path of a young man of taciturn, hypersensitive, dreamy character awaited him in Paris. To begin with, in a capital playing host at the time to so many foreign artists, he had great trouble finding a studio. He had to settle for a hotel on Boulevard Pasteur, but luckily his old and faithful friend Artigas was there to give him a hand. Thanks to Maurice Raynal, he met Pierre Reverdy and, finally, Tristan Tzara, who, haloed with the reputation of a destroying angel, was setting an astonished but skeptical Paris on its heels in the name of Dada. "That name Dada, the name that it pleased one of us to give it, has the advantage of being perfectly equivocal.... Dada is a state of mind. There is no Dada truth. It is enough to say a sentence for the contrary sentence to become Dada.... Dada fights you with your own reasoning" (André Breton, *Littérature*, no. 13, 1920).

Yet, already the tactical and amicable rapprochement between Tzara and Breton was showing cracks. For his part, Miró followed from a distance the demonstrations and events where the rattles and bells of those poets ready to change the world made a loud noise. However, he did attend the Festival Dada in the Salle Gaveau on 26 May 1920, where nobody stinted on contestation and everyone indulged in irony and planned provocation to his heart's content.

Beneath the young Miró's outward guise, glum and little inclined to communication, was a determined creature, a young wolf with long teeth, an aggressive fighter. In July 1920, he wrote to his confidant Ricart: "Never again Barcelona, that's flat. Paris and the country—to the day I die! I don't know why it is, but those who lose contact with the world's brain fall asleep and turn into mummies. In Catalonia no painter has ever attained his full growth.... One must become an international Catalan" (in Dupin, pp. 96, 98). In summer, however, he returned to Montroig, where he threw himself into his work, producing numerous canvases. Save for four still lifes, the lot of them would perish, destroyed by Miró himself.

Back in Paris again, toward the end of 1920 Miró found that a friend, the Spanish sculptor Pablo Gargallo, had been appointed professor at Barcelona's school of fine arts and for the duration of his absence was willing to rent to him his studio at 45, rue Blomet in the Fifteenth Arrondissement. A few days later, at one of the weekly gatherings organized by Max Jacob, author of the dazzling *Le Cornet à dés*, Miró made the acquaintance of André Masson, who, he learned, had just rented an atelier in the same building. Years later, Masson remarked that their meeting, a conjunction of two creative minds that would have important consequences, was "seemingly engineered by the hand of Providence" (in Dupin, p. 98).

In 1934, in an issue of *Cahiers d'Art* specially devoted to Joan Miró (9, nos. 1–4), the poet Robert Desnos recalled, without apparent nostalgia, that building whose glory was due not only to the remarkable characters who gathered there and succeeded each other as tenants but also to its proximity to the notorious Bal Nègre. This dance hall, made popular by the artists but frequented mostly by modest employees, had a marvelous jazz band. Only artists could so happily rationalize that, although the place was squalid, it was also "poetic." As Desnos remembered it, "That courtyard was something phenomenal for Paris, a grassy enclosure planted with a lilac tree which must still be flowering every year and with a vine that the manager, who had aesthetic pretensions, ripped out because 'it looked dirty.'... In the summer, birds chirped in that patio. In the winter, the snow remained pure there, and longer than elsewhere in Paris." Since then, the place has been demolished, replaced by a damp square haunted by the boccie players of the Fifteenth Arrondissement. To call the attention of chance passersby to this square, once the site of such pyrotechnics of the imagination, the public authorities in 1974 erected there a large copy of Miró's statue *Bird (Lunar)* (1944–46, cast 1966; plate 266) on a dull geometrical base of white stone.

In the early twenties, that block became the gathering place for Antonin Artaud, Desnos, Michel Leiris, Limbour, Jacques Prévert, Armand Salacrou, Roland Tual, and, though more briefly, for many others. These were the people who in a few years would group themselves around André Breton and, under the name of the Surrealists, embroil themselves in controversy.

If for most of the local denizens, material life was chancy or difficult, it was particularly so for Miró, who wrote later in "Je rêve d'un grand atelier" (1938) that "those were very hard times: the panes of the window were broken, my heater that cost me forty-five francs in the flea market would not work. However, the studio was very clean. I used to tidy it up for myself. Since I was very poor I could not afford more than one lunch a week." Dupin, who cites this (p. 99), comments that "all he had to help him 'hold out' were tiny remittances from his family, their size meant to convey to him disapproval of his staying in Paris, as well as of his determination to become a painter."

49. *Table with Glove.* 1921. Oil on canvas, 46 × 35¼″ (117 × 89.5 cm).
The Museum of Modern Art, New York. Gift of Armand G. Erpf

While such gestures, dictated by familial concern for a son's future, might hold some individuals back or even make them shift course, they had no such effect on the young Miró. Precisely because such pressures were excessive, they had the contrary effect. As everything shows, they simply incited him to pursue the experiment. He seems to have had a genuine need to prove himself, both to himself and to others. Dalmau, faithful to his promise, organized a show for him at the Galerie La Licorne in 1921, but it did not bring the triumph Miró had counted on. Not a single picture sold. Still, a substantial preface was written for the catalogue by an important critic, Maurice Raynal. His gesture was courageous as well as generous, for as an adherent above all of Cubism, he had the right to expect much from this young man who had drunk "often from the glass of Grandpa Cézanne" but who could be gruff and too independent. Raynal justly recognized his audacities and originality: "One point, however, does seem definitively won by Miró. From the way in which he treated his portrait, one senses that sentimentality will never drown out the pronounced taste he reveals for the sole play of forms and colors. That indication recognized, we must remark now that among the forms and colors Miró has in mind to reconcile, there often surge up conflicts he does not always succeed in pacifying. Instead of keeping them apart, the Justice of the Peace himself fights with the litigants.... Is it possible to say much about skill in connection with a temperament supported by a fertile imagination? The thought is not to be entertained. And Miró teaches us in a categorical fashion how much chance, with an artist gifted as he is, makes an efficacious contribution to the play of imagination."

Back in Montroig, Miró began a large canvas, 52 by 57⅞″ (132 by 147 cm), the largest he had yet attempted. This painting, *The Farm, Montroig* (plate 53), became the theater of a close combat, where every fraction of an inch would have to be won against a redoubtable enemy. It occupied Miró well into 1922. For either diversion or respite, he undertook other, apparently contradictory works during that time. Often, however, extreme complication brings with it also a need to simplify, to prune away the underbrush, the sheer accumulation, so as to bring order into the empty canvas step by close step.

Table with Glove

Thanks to its coherence, *Table with Glove* (plate 49) is a strong painting. It is ample, stable: a large circle strongly emphasized, a broad horizontal, a thick vertical prolonged by two diagonal lines supported on a field of parallels, a few objects reduced to the elementary shapes of cylinder and rectangle. A cane supplies a diagonal, balanced by the soft and rumpled shape of a glove and the two swaggering bowknots on the drawing portfolio. The forms speak an insistent language, each energetically set in place, arranged, totally exposed. They are surrounded and hemmed in by empty space. They struggle against its invasion and, by sheer force of presence, themselves seem to take on a menacing character. While Fernand Léger used a similar formula, his plain, unequivocal forms are not, as are Miró's, invested with such a disquieting character.

50. *Still Life with Rabbit (The Table)*. 1920. Oil on canvas, 51⅛ × 43¼″ (130 × 110 cm). Private collection, Zurich

45

Horse, Pipe, and Red Flower

Horse, Pipe, and Red Flower (plate 48) and *Still Life with Rabbit*, also known as *The Table* (plate 50), are among the works produced during that sojourn in Montroig. Miró seems to have poured into them everything he had seen in Paris that was still whirling around in his brain. While the Cubists had deliberately reduced their color range, many painters had soon reacted, feeling that however beautiful grays, blacks, and earth colors might be, in the long run they were too limited. They set about reintroducing color into painting. Robert Delaunay led the protest, which was earlier prefigured by Juan Gris. Too much austerity ends by tiring, and color inevitably reasserted its claims. Miró's natural vehemence took over again, though in other ways. After remaining blocked for several months, unable to work, a veritable frenzy seized him: all colors, all forms, all objects seemed to him necessary to his pictures. He piled up and jumbled together clearly defined shapes in complicated patterns. He left not a centimeter without a line, point, sign, curve, striation. He fragmented planes of color, threw himself into a debauch of ornamentation, clipped forms to bits and patched them together in his own way. Fortunately, in the dazzling still life with horse and pipe, the whole of it is nailed down firmly at the base by a large smooth zone of bright blue, which is no less indispensable to all this fertile agitation than is a base to sculpture. Nothing is more difficult than to contain an explosion, yet Miró managed it by sheer, passionate willpower. And even more clearly than in its predecessors, this work lets us see the energy its author deployed in contriving a pictorial space without resorting to the rules, precedents, and habitual tricks of classical, illusionistic painting.

The Table (Still Life with Rabbit)

This work (plate 50), which once graced the walls of a famous Zurich restaurant, marks a departure in another direction. Here, Miró worked with an informed strategy. The space defined by straight lines and angles is underpinned by a star made by the legs, carved and further ornamented by small irregular rectangles, of a "Louis-Philippe"–style table. These in turn rest on another light-colored star, in its way a negative of the one above it. Filled and empty space have the same hardness, are both solid, weighty, of equal density. The color is held to a sober register. Into this geometrical universe, Miró successfully integrated bright-colored vegetables and creatures with downy pelt, silky plumage, and moiré scales. On a surface stretched taut by vigorous lines and planes, he managed to introduce unexpected patches of color and notes of concrete observation: the fidgety rooster, the frightened rabbit tensing to jump away. Flagrant contradictions, yet Miró found the exact equilibrium and pinned down the fleeting instant, by definition unstable.

Because many of Miró's canvases were destroyed, we shall never know the experiments that misfired. In what he chose to preserve, however, can be seen a growing need for refinement, for clarification. *Still Life with Rabbit* is a work rich in possibilities; like a summit, it has many sides.

Standing Nude

Standing Nude (plate 51), formerly in the Penrose Collection, is as dry as it is hard. This woman with white wood breasts is none other than a Penthesilea silhouetted against the sky, dominating the Olympics podium and steeling herself to clash swords. Her ocher sportswoman's body, reduced to simplified, numbered forms, seems not very different in nature from the uprights, square, and black rectangle framing her. But her feet are as large as spreading palm trees, and one hand is lumberjack-size. These tell us how Miró thinks of her, and they add to our confusion, for behind it we sense animosity.

51. *Standing Nude.* 1921. Oil on canvas, 51⅛ × 37¾" (130 × 96 cm). Perls Galleries, New York

Portrait of a Spanish Dancer

Portrait of a Spanish Dancer (plate 52) is distinguished by a great asperity of forms. Although painted in Paris after a chromolithograph, it is no product of an exile's homesickness. With its assertive openness and its attention to detail in order to overlook none of the characteristics of a type, this metalized dancer becomes the archetype of the provocative woman, dancer or not, the kind to blow cigarette smoke into the face of any overconfident male. The evening tones of brown for the hair, the reds of passion for the bodice with its machine-stitched embroidery evoke beyond the shadow of an error venality and sexual parody.

Because they are formal investigations into aesthetic order, Miró's paintings are all coherent worlds in themselves, no less so when stretched by internal contradictions. Vehicles of their author's phantasms, they remain a grille, a filtering screen, a transposition of "reality" held at a distance.

This *Spanish Dancer* passed through the hands of Dalmau, Dr. Girardin, and Pierre Loeb, the celebrated dealer who began to exhibit Miró's works in 1925, to end in those of Picasso, and is now on view in the Louvre, together with Miró's *Self-Portrait* of 1919. While it ended up in distinguished company, the painting did nothing to improve Miró's needy situation in 1921. Registered letters were fired off from Montroig, but the legitimate owner, Dr. Girardin, probably deeming he had done enough in organizing a first and unproductive exhibition for the young painter, did not deign to reply: "He never gave me a sou" (to Raillard, 1977, p. 52).

The Farm, Montroig

Begun in Montroig in 1921, continued in Barcelona, *The Farm, Montroig* (plate 53) was finished in Paris in 1922. Although the handwriting remained "detailist" to the point of obsession, the picture is unlike the minutely particularized works of 1918. In this rigidly fixed universe, the expanse is immense, and the eye can roam free as far as the undulating line of the distant mountains. Yet the pictorial space contracts under the effect of the intense blue of the sky, which tends to hold back all the intermediary planes, to drive them toward the foreground. For its part, the foreground is itself conjured away; nothing more than a cornstalk indicates its presence. The house, shed, wash place, pump, chicken coop are soldered one to the other and treated with the same intensity, the same coloristic precision. They are painted without modeling and the calculated distancing of perspective, though the latter enters in the lower left by means of the furrows, the prepared terrain, and various other pretexts. Miró had to invent and lay out a horizontal plane on which all the many scattered objects could rest, however arbitrarily. Other elements—the flagstone pavement, the newspaper, the black circle around the tree—are drawn on the vertical for formal reasons alone.

52. *Portrait of a Spanish Dancer.* 1921. Oil on canvas, 26 × 22″ (66 × 56 cm). Musée du Louvre, Paris. Picasso Donation

53. *The Farm, Montroig.* 1921–22. Oil on canvas, 52 × 57⅞″ (132 × 147 cm). Collection Mrs. Mary Hemingway

54. *The Carbide Lamp.* 1922–23. Oil on canvas,
15 × 18⅛" (38 × 46 cm).
The Museum of Modern Art, New York

The light is artificial, the opposite of the Impressionists' living light, and the absence of chiaroscuro affirms a choice that Miró has made, which would hold for all his future work. The vertical plane of the house, whose every crack and fissure is conspicuous, responds admirably to the linear drawing of the henhouse, with its white wall and yellow surface bestrewn with signs, a multiplicity of odd objects. A tree between the two buildings delicately deploys irregular branches ending in umbels, leafy bouquets silhouetted against a sky where a silver sun burns. Three times the branches terminate in a cluster of three boughs, and such regularity in numbers and series, flagrant here but camouflaged almost everywhere else, assures the unity of the composition.

Each object is in itself a veritable treatise of observation, isolated but in no way desolate. The painter has invited us to a fête in honor of his land, Montroig, and each object has a long story to tell about his childhood. Despite the enormous effort of concentration that this canvas demanded from him, as he himself has said, no trace of fatigue or second thoughts and changes can be seen. The color, laid on with a light brush, delineates each thing: fissured wall, tree bark, the crosspieces of the henhouse, rafters in the sloping shed. It bespatters or, rather, considering its precision, punctuates the surface. An exacerbated taste for description has elicited a graphic delirium. This is one of Miró's prime traits, imperative for an understanding of his future works. Finally, there is another and particular way of feeling that we have already noted: a hierarchy of values. The small is as important as the large —a part such as the bark equals the tree—a most unusual jugglery with metonymy. In this way, Miró cuts through our habitual code of reference and communication, often to troubling effect.

Jacques Dupin pertinently remarked of *The Farm*, "While it is the end product and synthesis of Miró's first period, it contains in germ myriad possibilities to which he will come back later and give a more fantastic development. The artist himself regards *The Farm* as the foundation and key to all his work.... All that he still has to do is to find the necessary strength, patience, and daring to carry this magic transmutation of reality one step farther—but as here, taking his departure from the felt, experienced, known reality, which desire awakens and fertilizes" (p. 99).

Miró harbored great financial hopes for this picture. He smothered his deep repugnance and undertook the round of the picture dealers (incurring heavy costs for taxis, he did not fail to point out). One dealer proposed to cut the canvas in four, making pictures that would fit better in the average-sized Parisian apartment. For lack of anything better, Miró accepted the offer of the Jockey café at Montparnasse to display the picture for one day as a means of attracting clients and artists. Gustave Coquiot made a speech in front of the painting to present it to the public, but with no success.

Some years later, the poet Evan Shipman had the idea of acquiring it for Ernest Hemingway. The deal was sealed by the deposit of a small advance on the price of five thousand francs. When the date came around to pay the balance, Hemingway, Shipman, and John Dos Passos, with not a cent between them, undertook the rounds of the Montparnasse bars and restaurants to collect the sum. Once again *The Farm*—for which someone had just offered the dealer four times the asking price—departed in a taxi, filling with wind like a sail, and was taken off to the Paris home of its now legitimate owner Hemingway, who took the additional debt

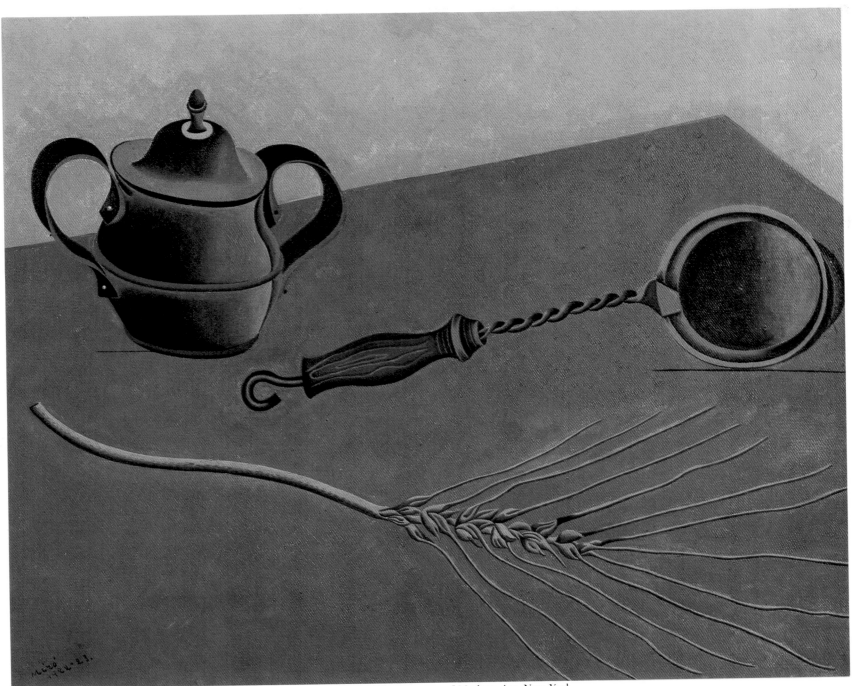

55. *The Ear of Grain.* 1922–23. Oil on canvas, 14⅞ × 18⅛″ (38 × 46 cm). The Museum of Modern Art, New York

56. *The Farmer's Wife.* 1922–23. Oil on canvas, 31⅞ × 25⅝″ (81 × 65 cm). Collection Mme. Marcel Duchamp

in his stride. Hemingway would never be parted from the picture. He wrote, "It has in it all that you feel about Spain when you are there and all that you feel when you are away and cannot go there. No one else has been able to paint these two very opposing things" (*Cahiers d'Art* 9, nos. 1–4, 1934, in G. di San Lazzaro, ed., *Homage to Joan Miró*, New York: 1972, p. 34).

Realism has been mentioned: the reality of the outer world or the inner world? Can one be separated from the other? If the phantasmic becomes the most important, it is because it is through it that the world is experienced.

When Miró left Montroig for Paris with this large, unfinished canvas among his luggage, he went so far as to take with him grass picked in the meadows of his native soil to help work out his picture. When it withered, he simply replaced it with samples from the Bois de Boulogne, although he regretted the difference between the two. For him, the grass represented Montroig and the whole cosmogony of feelings associated with that place, even though once it dried up another and alien plant could serve the same purpose. Perhaps what counted was only the idea of grass, and a concrete sampling was enough to set into movement, as if by magic, his affective memory and his imagination.

With Miró, the concrete and the magical, entire or in part, overlap. Between them exists at least a relation of propinquity. This observation, which reveals much about *The Farm*, will help us to better understand Miró the active Surrealist.

The pictures done before and after *The Farm* cast light on its composition. In Miró's development at the time, it formed a kind of enclave, an unexpected intrusion of the past, and yet, in the way its masses were distributed, very much of the present. While still minutely detailed, it differed in its proportions, and the objects were meant to be read in a different manner. They are isolated, calculatedly disposed, but linked by the *idea:* although all are rustic appurtenances, they are, above all, forms regarded in their own right, from their own point of view as well as the viewer's.

The Farmer's Wife, The Carbide Lamp, The Ear of Grain

In these three paintings (plates 54–56), that new distancing of the eye is acclimatized to the point of becoming fixed. All were begun in Catalonia and finished in France. With distance, the murmur of feeling grew fainter. Geography—and, perhaps, the example of Fernand Léger as well—seems to have strengthened the desire to retain from the world only geometry, even if the things depicted still wear, like garlands, recollections of the past. These three paintings are exercises in laying out angles and triangles. Curves contribute just enough diversion necessary to soften such rigor, to avoid the aridity of pure demonstration. The light yellow quadrilateral of *The Carbide Lamp* (plate 54) and the white circle cut across by a broken line in *The Farmer's Wife* (plate 56) prove that geometry in careful dosage serves to modify the usual attitude toward the concrete. Those objects—a stand for an iron, a two-handled kettle, a spike of wheat, and so on—are gigantic for the surface on which they are painted. Monuments of an agricultural civilization, they thereby lose their customary physiognomy and, with it, their identity. They exist to better conceal themselves within the cavity of an invented space.

1923-1925

The explorations undertaken by Miró since *Table with Glove* (1921; plate 49) had led him, stage by stage, through different themes, to *The Ear of Grain* (plate 55). That canvas and the others in the same series form an end point, a culmination. In them, Miró invented a space and then, by greatly enlarging a detail or the object itself, managed to modify appearances. The paintings unveil or, perhaps, conceal something else, and Miró was seeking what that was.

Officially, Surrealism was still in gestation. The building at 45, rue Blomet was a crucible at boiling point. Meetings and gatherings followed one on the other, exploded into discussions in which the entire world was rethought. The fertile minds of Artaud, Desnos, Leiris, Limbour, Prévert, Salacrou, Tual, and others, revolving around their captain, Breton, responded to the ideas flying around with passionate enthusiasm, intensity, and fantasy. These men were not content to react on paper or canvas. Their defiance of established values was lived in the flesh violently. Arrogant men, in subjecting themselves to dangerous experiments, they were willing to risk their own skins. From such ruthless experiments even Miró would emerge with strange drawings: "I made many drawings in which I expressed my hallucinations brought on by hunger. I came home in the evening without having eaten and noted my sensations on paper" ("Je rêve d'un grand atelier," *XXe Siècle* 1, no. 2, 1938).

With the 1924 manifesto, Breton signed the birth certificate of Surrealism, a great movement that would rapidly win an international audience and, in the decades to come, would spark off a renewal of individual and collective ways of thinking. The events of May 1968 would still bear its marks.

The basic idea of Surrealism, once accepted, changed the face of the world. It derived from the theories of Sigmund Freud, themselves based on therapeutic experience and whose keynote was the unconscious. The unconscious was conceived as fed by repressed as well as phantasmic desires, which remain the real needs motivating our acts. In practice, the ever-active unconscious activates and motivates the individual. By making the conscious mind its instrument, it seeks incessantly to manifest itself, to break free. The ideal terrain on which to observe it functioning is the dream. In 1900 Freud published his *Interpretation of Dreams*, and four years later he enriched his theory with *The Psychopathology of Everyday Life*, which delved closely into the mysterious irruption of the unconscious in acts that misfire or are unintentional, in slips of the tongue or memory and in wit itself.

The Surrealists were the first in France to recognize the immense import of the Freudian theories of our psychological apparatus. As a medical student, Breton had paid the master a visit in Vienna in 1921. The meeting was not very successful. It was a difficult time for Freud, attacks raining on him from all quarters. Breton found a man who dreaded the intrusions of the curiosity-seekers, which made him suspicious of all those who sought him out, and the account the poet wrote later reports his disappointment in too Dadaist a tone, though in time he had second thoughts and recanted.

Treatment of mental illness was no concern of the Surrealists. What interested them above all was gaining access to the irrational by means of the dream in a world and system of thought that reason and rationalism had led to disaster. The war they had just lived through had left them sick at heart and in desperate revolt. It seemed to them that the only valid reaction to the sciences and fine theories formulated by the same rationality that had led society into such horror was, first of all, to demolish everything through laughter and derision: whence Dada. In a second phase, they looked to a more constructive approach in which whatever had been censured and repressed, all the force and violence of freely expressed desires, would be integrated into human life: whence Surrealism. The union of night things and day things would give man a single aspect: "I have always been amazed at the way an ordinary observer lends so much more credence and attaches so much more importance to waking events than to those occurring in dreams" (André Breton, "First Manifesto," 1981, p. 11).

For the Surrealists, poetry had to have the strange and marvelous power of the dream. Just as dream images are always metaphorical, so the images the poet invents should assemble elements furthest from reality, and the more remote those elements are one from the other, the more they will be marvelous and freighted with force: "Let us not mince words: the marvelous is always beautiful, anything marvelous is beautiful, in fact only the marvelous is beautiful" (Breton, "First Manifesto," 1981, p. 14). This attitude places all power in the imagination.

Miró, in a letter to his friend Ricart, examined painting since Impressionism with the utmost lucidity and asserted, "I believe our 'school' will grasp the essentials of the painting of the future. It will be stripped of all concern for pictorial problems, it will vibrate in harmony with the pulse of the Spirit.... These modern analytical movements will ultimately carry the spirit into the light of freedom" (in Dupin, p. 81).

For Miró, the ideas, proposals, and heated struggle of his new friends came at just the right moment to reassure him about his own desires: painting liberated from the weight of tradition, from the interdicts of the sacrosanct rules applied and perfected by the Renaissance artists and thereafter enforced in the academies. Painting "stripped of all concern for pictorial problems" and, therefore, of illusion, constitutes a provocation. In periods of revolt, to kill off the fathers it is always necessary to harden one's positions. What Miró had to kill off above all was the illusions of his youth, for he had an excellent acquaintance with the painting of the past; he understood and appreciated it, as demonstrated in his conversations concerning the Louvre recorded by Pierre Schneider (1972).

But Miró did not accept rules without subjecting them to his own evaluation. He knew their historical value as elements of a time, sensibility, and conception of the world pertinent to a particular society. Each generation, as he saw it, has the duty to examine them anew and to revise them, as each generation is different. Tradition properly understood creates a transformation, and—no paradox intended—sometimes entails a rupture and a revolution. For all his extravagances, provocations, and even errors, Miró was a poet who never forgot that he was a painter. In the particular though international language that is painting, color and the plastic factor exist and are sufficient, in themselves, to establish communication and, ultimately, communion.

In theory, within the Surrealist context, the means of art, its grammar, and its aesthetic pretensions were meaningless. Instead, its fascination lay only in whatever burst the boundaries of rational associations and the conventions, in this way attaining the mysterious and marvelous. For the Surrealists, its value lay only in the sense of displacement and the deflagration the poet set off by the unsuspected juxtaposition of terms never intended to coexist but which, once brought together, produce a violent impact. "I believe in the pure Surrealist joy of the man who, forewarned that all others before him have failed, refuses to admit defeat, sets off from whatever point he chooses, along any other path save a reasonable one, and arrives wherever he can" (Breton, "First Manifesto," 1981, p. 46). Thus, Breton was led to imagine the "Surrealist object," one composed "entirely on the basis of all sorts of elements gathered from what is immediately at hand," a proposition accepted by many artists in the group, Miró among them. As early as 1928, Miró was content to reduce the *Spanish Dancer* (plate 107) to the mere apparition of a long hatpin piercing a feather in the center of a canvas. Later, he would give in to even more fantastical works, charged with violent aggressiveness.

Miró spent the summer of 1923 in Catalonia. By then it was clear that he could never separate himself psychologically from Montroig. That farmhouse, village, and landscape were indispensable to him to make contact again with the earth, from which—as he himself said, stamping the ground as he did so—he drew new strength through his very feet. This was his rationalization, and he firmly believed in it. Curious indeed are the connections that can be made between *madre* (Spanish for mother), *mare* (Catalan for mother), *mar* (Spanish for sea), *materia* (Spanish for matter), *terra* (Catalan for earth), *mater* (Latin for mother): a chain of interlocking metaphors leading finally to *ma terre* (French for my land) or *ma terra* (Catalan), in its many different senses. Perhaps Miró's unalterable need to return to that one special place—where pleasure, chagrin, reality were linked—arose from a compulsion for repetition. Purely on the symbolic plane, of course, it resembles the murderer's strange mania that seizes him after he commits the crime. Obviously, however, in the realm of painting, Miró had every right to commit the crime if he so desired, if it gave him pleasure: "When I wish to assassinate painting, it is as oil-and-vinegar painting, all that school cookbookery, the old-fashioned conception of painting" (to Georges Raillard, 1977). He would reiterate that notion in 1944 in a text published by Gaëtan Picon in *Carnets catalans* titled "From the Assassination of Painting to Ceramics," with the title written by his own hand in full capitals.

Thus it was at Montroig that Miró once again pulled himself out of a momentary block. And it was on that soil that he made the leap (the word is Jacques Dupin's) that permitted his true self to emerge. From his first works, his independence was obvious. He always knew how to preserve it, even against Surrealist orthodoxy. In his time, however, it was the only movement that could help him by receiving him into its bosom. The fact is, Miró was untouched by the abstract tendencies widespread at the time, represented by very great artists then still little known, including Wassily Kandinsky, Robert Delaunay, and Piet Mondrian. Invited to participate in events promoting abstraction, he properly refused, the style being alien to him. It was only with Klee, whom he had just discovered as if by chance, leafing through an album, that he felt any deep elective affinities. Klee had already prepared a terrain where Miró had decided to lay out his own wares and set up shop. But the difference between them was striking. Miró was an impetuous Catalan impelled one day to discover himself through vigorous gesture, Klee a man coiled away in the silent rumblings of his inner world, in love with the walls of his labyrinth, endlessly, delicately scoured bare. Miró exploded, Klee imploded.

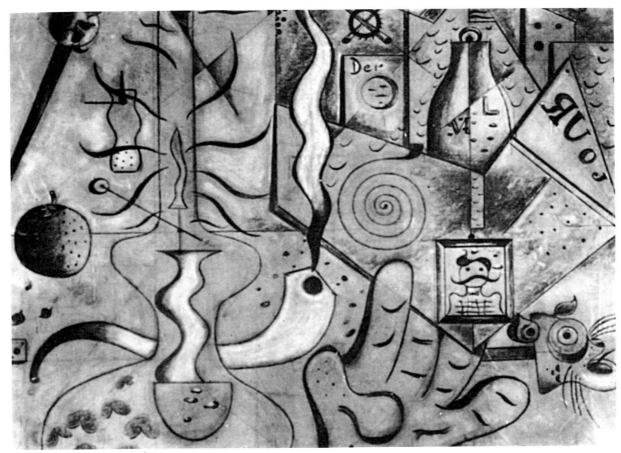

57. *The Kerosene Lamp.* 1924.
Charcoal, chalk, and tempera on
canvas, 31½ × 39″ (80 × 99 cm).
Private collection

58. *The Family.* 1924.
Charcoal and red chalk,
29½ × 41⅜″ (75 × 105 cm).
The Museum of Modern Art, New York

Preparatory Drawings

If not in overt contradiction, Miró was at least out of line with the Surrealist theories, as proved by his preparatory drawings. They are in no way the fruit of a spontaneous upsurging of an image refracted by the dream but rather the methodical, careful expression of a calculated delirium of the imagination. Between Surrealism and Miró, there was exactly the space of a dream, the difference between full tide and an eyedropper, between that which comes in bulk and that which is distilled. Each picture was prepared by more or less precise notes, then carried over onto canvas and transfigured by color. Some drawings were even squared up to facilitate the transfer. The structure of a Miró painting, moreover, always looks as if it has been calculated in terms of the individual project, of its pictorial effectiveness, and of what must be called its aesthetic. Numerous drawings were sometimes done, one after the other, modifying the first excited idea. These were—vile sacrilege from the Surrealist standpoint—corrected, freed of their dross. They did not obey the first promptings of the unconscious jotted down in the instant of their revelation. Because choices were made (anathema to the Surrealists), these works belonged to art, even if no one would or wished to see that at the time. As for their author, he was himself too wrapped up in working out his own problems, himself an onlooker too carried away by the strangeness of the spectacle.

Miró noted his ideas for pictures in sketchbooks. More or less summary rough drawings, attempts to define details, and sketches for compositions are jumbled together with notes, technical directives, maxims, first drafts of poems, and so on. The abandoned projects, successive states of a single idea, technical procedures jotted down as they occurred to him all reveal the movement of an imagination at once mobile and centered, always at work. Sometimes the "first thought" (but was it the first?) corresponds closely to the finished work, as in *Head of Catalan Peasant* (plates 78, 79). Other projects are wholly transformed, without, however, losing sight of the initial conception, as in *The Siesta* (plates 74–76). Still others afford a constant vision of motifs and composition: "In the sketch for *The Harlequin's Carnival* [plates 70, 73], the layout of the diagonals prepares even the distribution of the straight lines in the painting, although that visual approach remains a little irresolute. The notebooks let us penetrate into the field of the possible" (Pierre Georgel, preface to *Dessins de Miró*, exhibition catalogue, 1978–79).

The Tilled Field, Montroig (plate 60) signaled a new era, that of overt fantasia. In the order of creation, *Catalan Landscape* (plate 63), itself the precursor of *Head of Catalan Peasant*, is closely related. In *The Kerosene Lamp* (plate 57) and the large drawing *The Family* (plate 58), Miró ventured away from the repertory of objects alone to that of composite human figures. If such a step is easy enough today, at the time it was a difficult line to cross: any attack on the integrity of the human physical form was viewed as a violation.

The Tilled Field, Montroig

Every painting is a surface, every painting is a space—the geometrical figures and the forms the artist summons up, if they are to be brought together and united, must be reconciled with this conception. For all his unbridled invention, Miró did not go so far as to transgress that rigorous conceptual necessity. All his canvases are admirably balanced, with full areas calculated in relation to empty, lines effectively dividing the surface, forms corresponding and relating to each other spatially without jarring our eye and memory. In the essential respects, he obeys the natural laws of painting.

What astounds and disturbs us in Miró's work is the appearance of these regrouped objects and their aggressive character. If a tree bears an ear and in its leaves an eye, we must probably accept the fact that its trunk bleeds and its foliage is armed with formidable claws (plate 60). We see a blue mare, whinnying, suckling a frenetic colt, a bitter aloe tree transformed into a terrible saw. The motley carp come to the surface is on the verge of asphyxiation, the crouching dog with bristling hair has fallen victim to the black tide. A pine cone travels through the air, crackling. Stretched on a steel wire, like a smoker's pipe set up as target in the shooting booth of a village fair, a shark's fin moves across the space. This view of a worked field may be nothing other than a recollection of an Egyptian fresco in which Miró interprets derisively the bull Apis, originally a respected divinity, the animal-protector, symbol of fecundity. With its jerky marionettes and a décor cut out of the living quick of color, this scene is a veritable nightmare whose implacable stage manager is Miró himself.

Henceforth, like the Cubists and painters like Klee before him, Miró would use letters, syllables, phrases, numbers, even hypothetical mathematical operations in his drawings and paintings. In turn, Miró would enter into play the pure form of line and the outlandish nature of his graphisms and arabesques, impelling a new reading deep into his visual investigation. Perhaps another source should be added: folklore. Before industrialization overtook handicrafts, it was customary for the master worker to sketch out thoughts or aphorisms in the ground or on wood, paper, or glass. Miró inverted the order of things. In his work, the phrase in its graphic disposition very often becomes the picture itself. The garland of words within the space of the canvas becomes sufficient unto itself, a new plastic metonymy.

Two examples are *"Oh! Un de ces messieurs qui a fait tout ça"* (Oh! One of those gentlemen who has done all that) (1925; plate 61) and *"Un Oiseau poursuit une abeille et la baisse"* (A Bird pursues a bee and brings it down) (1926; plate 59), whose preparatory drawings were followed almost to the letter. In its painted version, the latter has been given the "feminine" attractions of color, which its text, despite its wordplay (*baisser* suggests the word *baiser*, a vulgarism for the sexual act), particularly seems to suggest, whereas the other work remains more evasive. (In the nineteenth century, Charles Blanc still seriously asserted that drawing is masculine, color feminine.)

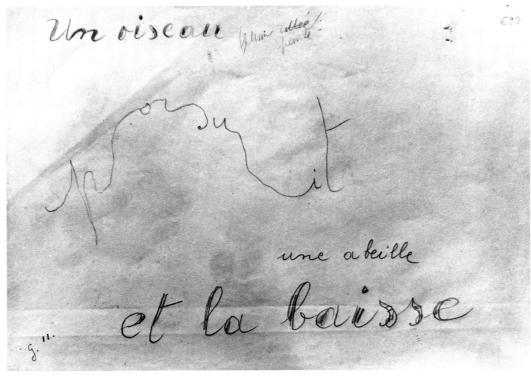

59. Study for "*Un Oiseau poursuit une abeille et la baisse.*" 1926. Pencil, 7⅞ × 10⅜" (20 × 26.4 cm). Fundació Miró, Barcelona

Catalan Landscape (The Hunter)

In *Catalan Landscape (The Hunter)* (plates 62, 63), impertinent forms—cones, squares, triangles, disks, tadpoles, mosquitos, and dragonflies, some armed with wormlike tentacles, others with waxed mustaches—move irritably and excitedly against a red and yellow ground separated by an undulating shorelike line. This first version, in a way, of *Head of Catalan Peasant* (1925; plate 79) looks like a Bastille Day set piece fit for fireworks. It also contains the first elements of *Maternity* (1924; plate 69) in the simple horizontal line that runs through an egg (foreground) and is stretched to breaking point by two cast-iron plaques of different colors. An important element of *Catalan Landscape* is a word, written large in a handsome, round hand and well laid out. In the preparatory drawing it was "Sardine," written horizontally; here it is on the bias and amputated of a syllable: "Sardine" has perhaps become *sardana*, the Catalan national dance. But, as in a rebus, Miró has mischievously placed just above it a grill for frying fish, which does seem to urge the first reading. Whichever it is, the uncertainty aroused by the word and its very meaning opens the way to poetical ambiguity.

Suddenly, in Miró's new paintings, the world explodes, becoming a phantasmagoria. The separate dominions are abolished, the categories so scrupulously established by the specialists are jumbled. The universe is in disorder or, at the least, it no longer respects the established order most of us accept: it tends toward disorder, if not chaos. It is another proposition altogether, in which elements that should remain alien meet, unite, and together run riot. But the mind is so constituted that in any representation in which the artist indulges in this game of Aunt Sally at a fair, he owes it to himself to invent an order, a space where even disparate forms find a coherence. Incoherence, do with it what you will, does not belong to art.

Portrait of Madame K., Spanish Dancer, The Gentleman, Maternity

Even if the order implied here is arbitrary, these pictures (plates 68, 67, 72, 69) must be related: the same signs reoccur and reverberate, the same spirit guides the artist's hand. Their subjects or themes must be approached indirectly, symbolically, although the signs are not so esoteric that they completely camouflage the sexual obsession behind them.

To ferret out the latent image concealed behind the manifest image in the dream, Freud made use of the method of free association. As a way of unmasking the unconscious desire giving rise to the metaphorical images of the dream, the analysand is encouraged to express spontaneously and without control by rationality or moral constraints whatever ideas come to mind. These paintings by Miró, even if prepared by numerous drawings, stem from just such a suspension of control by reason—a difficult task, because logical thought and social propriety exert heavy counterpressures.

Despite their titles, transposed or radically disfigured to throw us off the track, these pictures can be regarded as veritable psychological self-portraits. To evoke maternity as an immense pair of scissors is all too significant, even if, out of politeness, despair is clothed in humor (plate 69). In its simplicity, this picture is so artistically successful and fresh that our pleasure and visual satisfaction intermingle, leading us to forget how razor-sharp the instrument is and what it could cut off if, for an instant, the counterweight should go out of balance and the blades snap shut. Of course, there is never a single interpretation for a dream. The metaphorical material is supple and multilayered, the meaning tends to become diffuse, the coloration changes. Thus, Jacques Dupin considers this painting "one of the purest and most successful of all Miró's reductions of reality to symbols," and with genuine poetic warmth sees in it "an inequality of weight

60. *The Tilled Field, Montroig.* 1923–24. Oil on canvas, 26 × 37″ (66 × 94 cm). Solomon R. Guggenheim Museum, New York

61. *"Oh! Un de ces messieurs qui a fait tout ça."* 1925. Oil on canvas, 51⅛ × 37⅜" (130 × 95 cm). Private collection, Tokyo

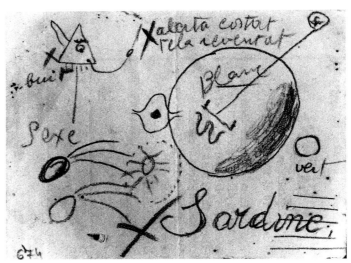

62. Study for *Catalan Landscape (The Hunter)*. 1923–24. Pencil and red chalk, 3⅜ × 4¼" (8.5 × 10.8 cm). Fundació Miró, Barcelona

sanctioned by the mysterious laws of creation—laws of which Miró gives us...an extraordinarily pure elucidation" (Dupin, pp. 146, 147). If our respective interpretations do not converge, neither do they cancel each other; on the contrary, they support each other.

To draw up an inventory of the signs and figures, assign the attributes composing them, and extricate the particular character of each as well as the interlacings of their meanings could be done only by the person directly involved, and that belongs to the secret he has no intention of unveiling.

The Harlequin's Carnival

Fantasia, fête: *The Harlequin's Carnival* (plates 70, 73) is a veritable delirium—a saltimbanques' fair, a religious procession among the protozoans, an unbridled pantomime that takes its contortions and vivid colors from a remote colonial and baroque Spain. Within this classical gray and ocher box, everything is unfixed save a table and a window open on a night-blue sky where comets flicker. The curtain has just gone up, and a squad of yellow insects and animals in disguise, cut out of scintillating fragments of tin cans gone over with aniline blue, disport themselves in flea-circus hops. Dice spill over with malice, leeches stand erect, roasting spits clash swords, a besotted Catalan peasant bawls, guitar in hand, blue moon and red sun, telescoped, squint in astonishment. The eyes cannot believe their ears. Luckily, a ladder sporting a flag offers escape from the hubbub, with its unruly mechanisms.

The year 1925 was distinguished by this devilry, this marvelous, marvelously free spectacle. No man is so withdrawn that one day he cannot burst out in laughter, although the laughter may be strident and strike a false note...

Jacques Viot, a friend from rue Blomet looking after Miró's interests, organized an exhibition at the Galerie Loeb from 12 to 27 June 1925. *The Farm, Montroig* (plate 53) and several works done between 1921 and 1924 were shown. Benjamin Péret wrote the catalogue preface: "...'I want to see the tree with the sardine.' I sent him to Joan Miró who has, someplace, a precious plantation of mysterious trees that sing heroic symphonies on funeral days." The invitation bore the signatures of all the members of the Surrealist group, and a huge crowd attended the opening. Viot reported, "The paintings on the wall dumbfounded those who could get a look at them, but I think that the artist amazed them even more, because nobody could figure out any connection between his works and his person. Miró made an enormous effort to make himself attractive....He wore an embroidered waistcoat, gray trousers, and white spats. He was profuse in paying compliments, but so afraid he might overlook somebody that he almost gave an impression of anxiety" (in Dupin, p. 154).

In November, Miró contributed three pictures, *The Harlequin's Carnival* among them, to an exhibition of Surrealist painting, including also works by Picasso and Klee, in the same gallery. The preface to the catalogue was written by Breton and Desnos. Thus, he became entrenched in the Surrealist group, but he continued to hold them at arm's length.

63. *Catalan Landscape (The Hunter)*. 1923–24. Oil on canvas, 25½ × 39½″ (64.8 × 100.3 cm). The Museum of Modern Art, New York

64. *Dialogue of the Insects.* 1924–25. Oil on canvas, 25⅝ × 36¼″ (65 × 92 cm). Private collection, Paris

65. *Female Bather.* 1924–25. Oil on canvas, 28¾ × 36¼″ (73 × 92 cm). Collection Michel Leiris, Paris

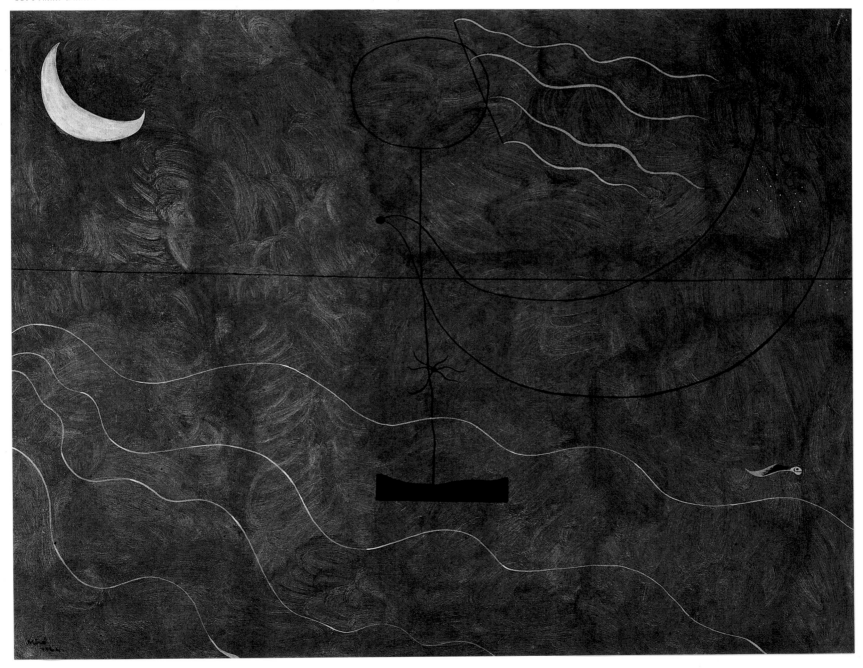

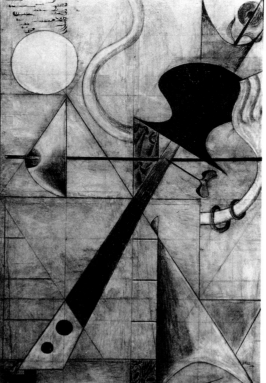

67. *Spanish Dancer.* 1924.
Oil, charcoal, and tempera
on canvas, 36¼ × 28¾″ (92 × 73 cm).
Private collection, France

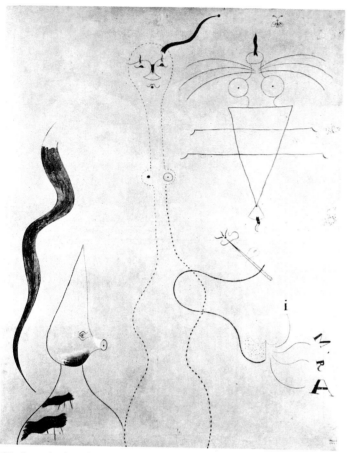

66. *Portrait of Madame B.* 1924. Oil and charcoal on canvas,
51⅛ × 37¾″ (130 × 96 cm).
Collection M. William, N. Copley, New York

68. *Portrait of Madame K.* 1924. Oil and
charcoal on canvas, 45¼ × 35″ (115 × 89 cm).
Private collection, France

If audacity is a franchise taken for granted nowadays, especially in literature, it was not so in 1925. There was indeed stuff for scandal then. The Surrealists were delighted to provoke it and to untie the corset strings of prudery. However, looking below the peaceful if not innocent surface of painting over the centuries, many examples of insubordination to the morals of the dominant group can be found. Artists have not hesitated to strip their gods and nymphs, amid trees and groves, even of their undergarments of implication. If the form changed in the course of time, the heart of the matter remained eternal, as did the rationalizations given, as evidenced by the following conversation between Miró and Georges Raillard in 1977 (pp. 186–87):

"For me, when I make a large female sex organ it is as a goddess, as the birth of humanity."

"But when the sex organ is a spider and seems about to devour...?"

"That thing like a spider you are talking about, that's really the hair. That looks like spiders, that turns wicked."

"We're a long way from the goddess of fecundity."

"It's a fecundity, but menacing all the same."

"Why is that?"

69. *Maternity.* 1924. Oil on canvas,
35⅞ × 29⅛″ (91 × 74 cm).
Private collection, London

"Ah, well...That came in spite of myself...You see what humanity is, always menacing, on the right and the left, above and below, we are threatened."

"No erotic harmony between man and woman!"

"No, there's nothing erotic. At times, I have represented coitus, not much. And the male personage is always menaced by the female. The man will be swallowed up by that menacing woman."

"Breton talked with you about that, himself the prophet of woman as protectress, mediatrix..."

"No, no. I think that Breton overlooked that. I have made a canvas with coitus by moonlight, a large male sex organ with a line which is the coitus, the physical contact of man with woman."

"Representation of eroticism? Or reminder that every canvas, every work is erotic, sexual movement mimed?"

"More than a sexual movement, if I make a big male sex organ with testicles, it is something sacred for me. It is not erotic. It is like the seed of a tree that pushes up under the ground, the rain makes the seed sprout and that makes a tree. It is the birth of a tree. For that birth, it is the sex organ that comes to my mind most spontaneously, yes."

"The male organ has, in general, something to attach to, while your female organs traverse the canvas, here and there, like night birds, black and red."

"That's true. For the colors, in principle, the red range represents the open organ and the black range the closed organ."

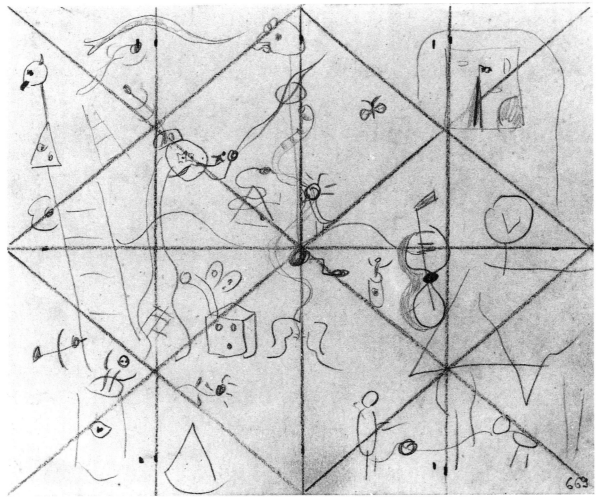

70. Study for *The Harlequin's Carnival.* 1924–25. Pencil and red chalk,
6⅝ × 7⅝″ (16.7 × 19.3 cm). Fundació Miró, Barcelona

71. *Painting.* 1925. Oil on canvas, 44⅞ × 57⅛″ (114 × 145 cm).
Private collection, Chicago

72. *The Gentleman.* 1924. Oil on canvas, 20½ × 18⅛″ (52 × 46 cm). Kunstmuseum, Basel

73. *The Harlequin's Carnival.* 1924–25.
Oil on canvas, 26 × 36⅛″ (66 × 93 cm).
Albright-Knox Art Gallery, Buffalo, N.Y.

1925-1927

Reason is tyrannical, it brandishes its rod over all our activities. To drive it off in order to reach the unconscious is a difficult undertaking. To get rid of it, an exercise had to be invented, and, since playing games strikes no one as serious, nothing would serve better than a game. In 1925 the Surrealists, as a group, invented *Le Cadavre exquis* (The Exquisite Corpse): "a game with folded-over papers which consists in having a sentence or drawing composed by several persons without any of them being able to take into account the collaboration or collaborations preceding theirs" (André Breton, *Dictionnaire abrégé du Surréalisme*, 1938). Once more, what counted here was not the aesthetic value but poetic freedom, pleasure, revelation.

Even if Miró rarely took part in the game, it is no less important to know that around him his friends were fully involved in it. He himself preferred to rely on metaphor, which he found familiar, natural. André Masson, I think, said that of all the members of the group Miró was the most naturally Surrealist. For him his game, his source of images, was the ceiling of his miserable studio: "I saw shapes in the chinks in the walls, and shapes on the ceiling, mainly on the ceiling" (to Gaëtan Picon, 1976, p. 72; p. 73).

The year 1925 was a fertile one, with an abundant harvest. Miró was exploring his idea. Like a musician, he had found a motif and was drawing from it all the inventions possible. Many of his backgrounds were blue—"aerial oceans"—or a much modulated reddish bronze, across which glided long lines, strict, undulating, or broken, and sparkling splashes of whites, reds, or greens. The space of the painting was immense, vast as a sea of clouds glimpsed through an airplane porthole. A few isolated plastic signs between them shared the surface of his canvas. By a kind of wizardry, a line behaved like a cut and left a sensitized zone all around it; a spot acted like a drop of oil on blotting paper, overflowing its contours to surround itself with a wave.

All these features have something of the physical: the line scratches like a wound, its trail burning or dry; the spot impacts like a violent blow that leaves an aching spot in the injured flesh, or then again like a needle prick. And Miró plays with the element of surprise, as Klee so admirably does with the unexpected. He catches whatever is in flight, snaps his net tight on the butterfly in its seesawing trajectory. Expert entomologist, he fixes it on his canvas by pinning it down. He always held in reserve a marvelous faculty of knowing just where to place each line, each color, in the surest and most expressive manner. His sureness was infallible. Considered thus, the whole of his work is a perpetual wonder.

This is a good place to recall that admirable training for the eye that he probably discovered very early. Still a child, he used to go to the museum of early art, which housed superb Romanesque frescoes. The earliest dated from the ninth century, gathered from sanctuaries and hermitages throughout Catalonia. Pious and truly inspired hands saved them from the damp and from tourists' graffiti. The small isolated churches poised on rocky mountains did not, however, lose their ancient treasures, since respectful copies replaced the originals preserved in the museum.

God in glory, the Virgin reigning on earth as in heaven, the Evangelists represented by their symbolic animals, eagle, bull, and lion, processions of saints, martyrs tortured by fire or stake, angels with wings studded with eyes, all these covered walls and vaults. Earth colors, blues, ochers, reds, yellows are spread across white backgrounds. Come from the East by way of Byzantium, these flat silhouettes, without modeling, appear appliquéd on the wall surfaces. They are draped in cloths that produce broken folds, concentric waves, intercrossing lines. Lacking shading entirely, their colors hammer at the eyes, and their curves, straight lines, colored areas are organized around a rhythm as authoritarian as a drumbeat. These figures with eyes of shadow are not likenesses but ideas, lending an image to what in truth cannot have one: transcendence.

To speak of influence would be too simplistic. One must go further. These frescoes spread out before Miró's childish eyes elicited from him the intensity of an instant commitment. Painting and its lines and associated colors were bound up for him with the pulsing of his drumming heart. Traveling under different forms,

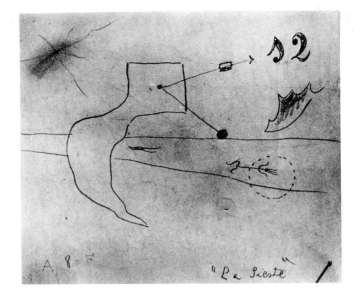

74, 75. Studies for *The Siesta*. 1925. Pencil, 6⅝ × 7½″ (16.7 × 19 cm). Fundació Miró, Barcelona

sometimes taking shortcuts, sometimes meandering, his desire finally came to a stop before him, although he was not yet aware of it, and this may have been his great secret, which, through painting, he experienced to the end. In the final analysis, that early art did not represent what its subject appeared to put forward. With no need of a covering pretext, the forms and colors and the relationships created between them, the space they suggested constituted painting, the kind of painting to which Miró aspired. Degas once confided to Stephane Mallarmé that he had ideas for a number of sonnets, at which the poet informed the painter that poems are made with words. This anecdote, accurate or not, carries a meaning equally applicable to painting.

Miró was a man who took care. Like all who are sparing of words, he was attentive to ritual. He could not bear an anarchic or disorderly studio. He kept to his way stubbornly, outwardly imperturbable whatever inner disarray he may have experienced. Once again he quit Paris for his refuge in Catalonia, in a way his *querencia*, the imaginary place every bull finds in the arena where it withdraws after attack, feeling itself safe there.

When Jacques Viot offered him a contract that would finally permit him to hold his own, Miró promptly rented a new atelier in Paris, at 22, rue de Tourlag in Montmartre, where he had for neighbors the poet Paul Éluard, the painters Max Ernst and René Magritte, and the poet-sculptor Hans Arp, with whom he would enjoy a particularly close friendship. In 1928, on the initiative of Pierre Loeb, the large landscapes were exhibited at the Galerie Georges Bernheim, rue du Faubourg-Saint-Honoré. Two years later, E. Tériade, founder of the superb review *Verve* and then collaborator of Christian Zervos, published in *Cahiers d'Art* a "documentary" on recent painting (5, no. 2, p. 76). In an article subtitled "The Literary Reaction," he wrote: "The imperceptible breeze of the Orient caught by the musical waves of Kandinsky and Klee, Chagall's freely imaginative contribution, swollen with poetry, quietly crossed the hitherto closed frontiers of Paris and infiltrated patiently, not without a certain wiliness, into the pictorial preoccupations of those young men who for the time being found in themselves no taste for the secret savor of the Cubist constructions. Moreover, they underwent this imperious influence

without any deep knowledge of its origin. And because they wished to express their overflowing wealth of poetry instantly, they disdained the truly mysterious, because living, lyricism that emanates from the man and the painter in the creation of Picasso, Braque, or Matisse in favor of the facile mystery, fabricated most often with elements assembled in haste, no matter where, no matter how, and adorned only with a disarming candor."

Among those facile fabricators of a candid mystery could be counted, it seems, Joan Miró.

The Siesta

The first idea for *The Siesta* (plate 76) appears in a drawing (plate 74). The sun shoots out its flames, mosquito-birds sweep the sky, a five-legged donkey tied to a tree pulls at its chain, butterflies fly in small squadrons. A house, a sundial, a woman stretched out, an empty *porron*, an abandoned accordion, all dream under the crushing heat. Near the mountain, by the seashore, four children dance the *sardana*. Bright light proclaims this the hour of repose.

A second drawing (plate 75), in an abrupt departure, renders the exact idea of the final painting. All secondary details have been discarded, and all that remains is the fundamental structure of the painting: a leafy and rumpled green sun, the horizon line, a mountain in the shape of a blue umbrella, the sundial's yellow-tipped hand pointing to the number 12 (noon). The children are replaced by a stylized sign, their round dance by a dotted circle. The house and the woman's body have been brusquely telescoped to compose an extravagant livid mermaid-cum-hammerhead shark standing out against a blue ground as rhythmic and wavy as the sea. All the elements of the earlier naive composition have been removed or condensed, each bears the other's attributes, and metaphor has replaced labored description. And when metaphor appears, the unconscious and poetry knock at the door.

In the lower left corner of the second drawing, Miró noted A (=*azul*, blue), 80 F (the standard format of the canvas). His working procedure here was not rigorous, although elsewhere he found invention flowing effortlessly from the first sketch.

76. *The Siesta.* 1925. Oil on canvas, 38⅛ × 57½" (97 × 146 cm). Musée National d'Art Moderne, Centre Georges Pompidou, Paris

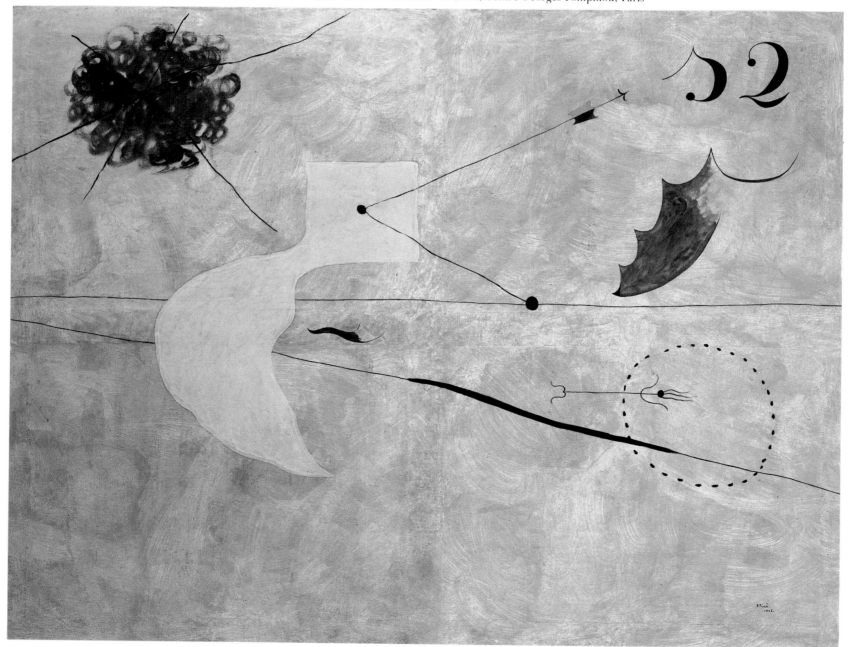

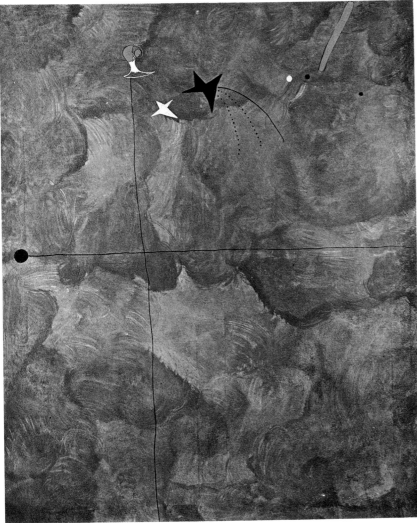

77. *Head of Catalan Peasant.* 1925. Oil on canvas, 57½ × 44⅞″
(146 × 114 cm). Private collection, Stockholm

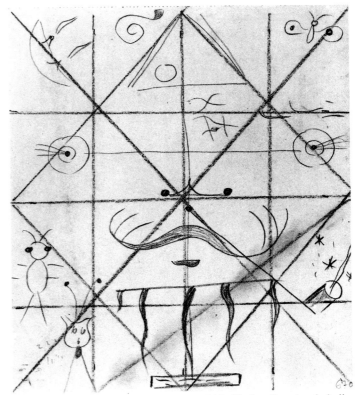

78. Study for *Head of Catalan Peasant.* 1923–25. Pencil and red chalk,
7⅝ × 6⅝″ (19.3 × 16.7 cm). Fundació Miró, Barcelona

Head of Catalan Peasant

Rainer Maria Rilke believed that a poem had found its form when there was nothing left to prune away. This very witty canvas (plate 77) confirms his notion. In 1925, Miró could scarcely have reduced his means further. Two major intersecting lines that seem to breathe, as he had intended, are enough to keep alert a large, agitated surface of intense cerulean blue. All but one of all the spots of color, red, white, and black, are deliberately concentrated in the upper third. Two forces confront each other: one, that of the lines, is lively, active; the other, of the clouds over the sea, is slow. Their dialogue with the picture ground continues to the lower border of the canvas. Miró's natural bent toward a proliferation of feverish forms here finds its antidote in this considerable economy of means.

While many years separate it from the canvases of 1961 titled *Blue I, II,* and *III* (plates 240, 244), works considered difficult, this canvas is close to them in spirit. They all raise the same major issue: a line (but which line?), a spot (but which spot?) should be able to live with a large space and to stretch it taut on condition that they have been correctly plotted and precisely positioned. The painters of ancient China were supreme masters of the art of resolving such relationships, but it is scarcely familiar to the Western sensibility.

Years later, Miró would find in certain American painters, themselves influenced by the Far East, confirmation of what he bore within himself from the start. He probably had to make that geographical and cultural detour to see clearly and to recognize elsewhere what was so very close to him. Such is the toll that anxiety demands from the imagination.

Head of Catalan Peasant

Preceded by a single drawing (plate 78), this picture (plate 79) needed only color added to its initial concept, although in its definitive form almost all of the anecdotal details have been eliminated. It would be summed up, against a transparent yellow and blue ground, in the red shape of the *baretina* (the peasants' popular headgear) and the gently waving ocher oriflammes, which may stand for plowed furrows or, perhaps, the Catalan armorial blazon of bloody fingers against a gold ground.

Miró aspired to become an international Catalan. These paintings of 1925–26 and others as well, including the *Blue* pieces of 1961, show the long peregrination he had to make before again setting foot in his Catalonia, which he truly never left.

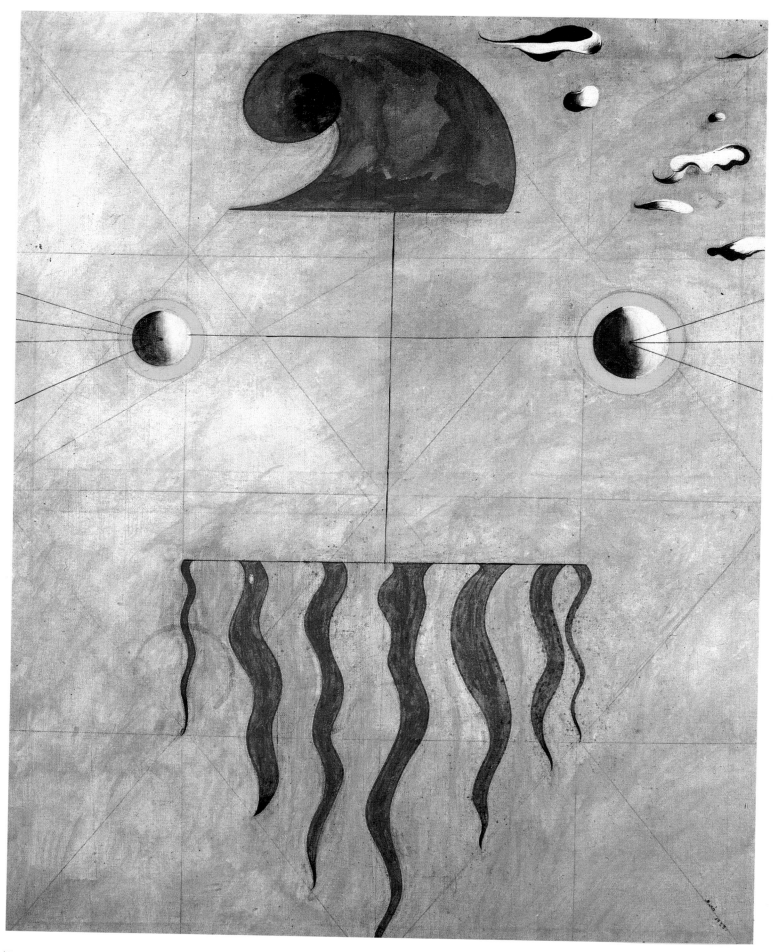

79. *Head of Catalan Peasant.* 1925. Oil on canvas, 35⅞ × 28¾" (91 × 73 cm). Private collection, London

80. *The Farmers' Meal.* 1925. Oil on canvas, 15 × 18⅛" (38 × 46 cm)

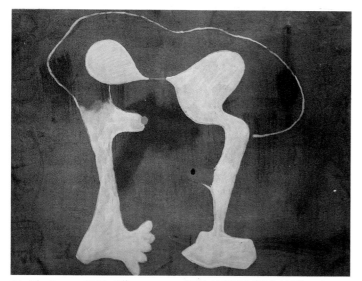
81. *The Lovers.* 1925. Oil on canvas, 28½ × 35⅜" (72.5 × 90 cm)

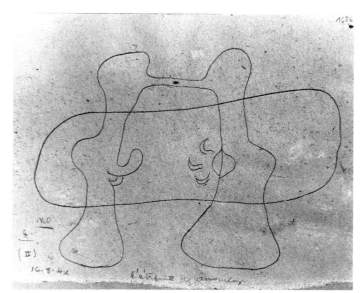
82. *The Lovers' Embrace.* 16 August 1942. Pencil, 9⅞ × 11¾"
(25 × 30 cm). Fundació Miró, Barcelona

The Farmers' Meal, The Lovers, The Check

The Farmers' Meal (plate 80) may have preluded a series of canvases titled *The Lovers* (plates 81, 82). The latter is an important theme in Miró's work, to which he would return often, never at a loss for new variations on the image of the couple. The partners draw close, move away, unite. Floating in a universe without end, they act without joy, shamelessly exhibiting themselves. Gnomes with sex organs erect or spread open, they belong not to humankind but to the strange category of hippocampi.

   Produced in Paris, all these canvases, including the enigmatic, dancelike *The Check* (plate 83), have something new in their execution. They bear the signs of swift gestures, of decisions ripely pondered and then executed quickly. The brushwork is all of a same flow, without second thoughts or smudges. The grounds are quickened by lively movements realized through keen concentration, showing neither hesitations nor dead space. Shoulder, elbow, arm, wrist, hand work all of a piece. Our eyes easily perceive that this group of works constitutes a unity, and that unity is mental, evidence of a moment when Miró felt confident of himself. These pictures exude from his inner being, from a single

secret source, from (to use a devalued word) the same inspiration. In his marvelous modulated backgrounds, Miró loses himself, limited only by the format of the canvas itself. In themselves, these grounds are paintings, traps for our eyes, looking glasses ordained to be passed through, to disclose, on their other side, perhaps nothing, perhaps the absence that knows no remedy.

The Circus Horse

In those years, Miró did a number of paintings on the theme of the circus horse (plates 84, 85). It is only logical to imagine that one can make out that creature in the earliest of those works. Initially, the horse is obstinate, erect, it plants itself firmly, its mane bristling, outside the circus ring and refuses to enter it. Then, as the theme develops, it becomes transformed. The artist's attention turns elsewhere. What does a circus horse do? It goes around and around. A slender line, hesitant, like a track left in the sawdust of the ring, retraces the circumvolution of its course, reading in it its

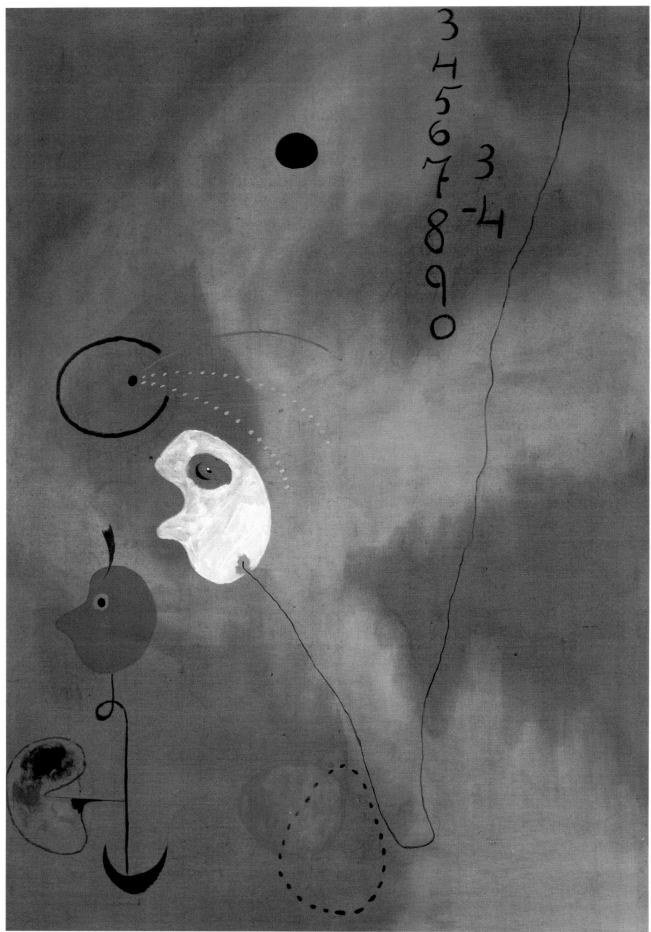

83. *The Check.* 1925. Oil on canvas, 76¾ × 51⅛″ (195 × 130 cm).
Musée National d'Art Moderne, Centre Georges Pompidou, Paris

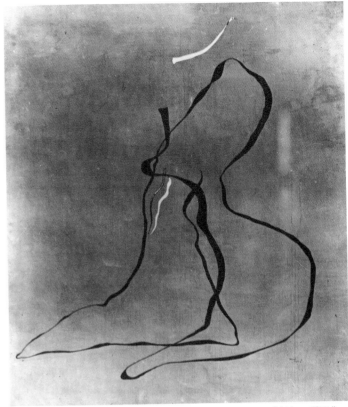

84. *The Circus Horse.* 1927. Oil on canvas, 38⅛ × 51⅛″ (97 × 130 cm). Private collection, Belgium

85. *The Circus Horse (The Lasso).* 1927. Oil on canvas, 51⅛ × 37⅜″ (130 × 95 cm). Fogg Art Museum, Cambridge, Mass. Gift of Joseph Pulitzer, Jr.

mulish waywardness, brusque halts, agitated lurches forward. In the long run, it becomes something mechanical, a rocking horse: criticism or evocation of childish memories? In its new state, it is impassive, indifferent to the clacking whip, now rendered useless against its wood.

Finally, the instrument of its subjugation becomes the subject to the point of invading the entire surface: before our eyes, the long sweep of the whip coils, uncoils, lashes, punishes the sudden swerves, the stubborn balking of the now-hypothetical horse. A long, flowing curved line, harmonious in its course, will oppose any unforeseen capricious leap. The lasso, a solid thong of hemp or leather, there is deployed to break the last vain impulse toward liberty. At last a line, a single line but energetic and superb in its development, tells its tale of domination. Visually, on the plane of painting, it is an arabesque that says nothing save what it is itself: a magnificent graphism in an undefined space where it can unfurl harmoniously; a "line that breathes," according to Miró's own expression.

The Landscapes

During the summer months of 1926 and 1927, Miró's native soil, light, even heat seem to impregnate a series of landscapes in which the savor of the fantastic vies with the aroma of the grotesque (plates 86–90). Many are divided by a straight or wavy line into two zones, one light, one dark. The light zone is generally at the top, so we take it to be the sky, but sometimes, as in *Person Throwing a Stone at a Bird* (plate 89) or *Dog Barking at the Moon* (plate 86), the

upper zone is the dark one. The color is most often smooth, opaque, applied with care to rule out the accidents of paint or effects of the hand—in effect, what the academics call "well painted." The same formats are repeated; Miró quickly decided on the relation between the size of the canvas and the form of his painting and usually retained it. Most of his paintings were preceded by dynamic shorthand notes, in which, without fuss, the hand made itself the obedient servant of the mind in action. His hand neither raced ahead nor lagged behind, but set and kept the right pace.

The light in these *Landscapes* is ardent, abrupt, dry, provoking no modulation in color, no cast shadow, no trace of the slightest penumbra. The precisely contoured forms look as if they were cut out with scissors from colored cardboard. Generally few in number, they are largely isolated from each other, remote, abandoned in a space that seems immeasurable, crushing. There they move about, twist and turn, shoot up like jack-in-the-boxes and seem to be expecting an omnipotent hand to promptly put them back where they came from. Clad in violent colors, they punctuate the surface, related in often extravagant irregular triangles. The sum total of all these traits makes these landscapes bizarrely into inner fields of delirious actions, developing in a box whose sides are the edges of the canvas.

Yet the things pictured are simple, things one comes upon while out walking. For the landscape also called *The Grasshopper* (plate 88), Miró confided to Gaëtan Picon: "Yes, my starting point really was a grasshopper.... for the painting I added the sun on which the inverted shapes of the mountains are outlined, and the ladder of escape. That's a grasshopper all right! I was in the country

86. *Dog Barking at the Moon.* 1926. Oil on canvas, 28¾ × 36¼″ (73 × 92 cm). Philadelphia Museum of Art. The A. E. Gallatin Collection

87. *Landscape with Serpent*. 1927. Oil on canvas, 51⅛ × 76¾″
(130 × 195 cm). Private collection, France

88. *Landscape (The Grasshopper)*. 1926. Oil on canvas, 44⅞ × 57½″
(114 × 146 cm). Private collection, Brussels

89. *Person Throwing a Stone at a Bird*. 1926. Oil on canvas,
29 × 36¼″ (73.7 × 92 cm). The Museum of Modern Art, New York

90. *Landscape (The Hare)*. 1927. Oil on canvas,
51⅛ × 76¾″ (130 × 195 cm).
Solomon R. Guggenheim Museum, New York

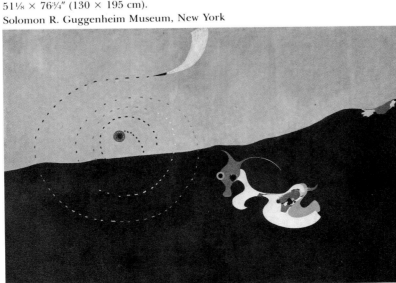

round Montroig, and I studied crickets and all sorts of insects...."
(*Carnets catalans*, 1976, pp. 78–79; pp. 75–76). Mysterious
imagination, which, once the brakes are released and the mind
wittingly allowed to run free, shakes off the customary associations
hardened through long use and ends up prospecting new and
virgin lands in its fabulous domain. While André Breton believed
"in the future resolution of these two states, dream and reality,
which are seemingly so contradictory, into a kind of absolute
reality, of *surreality*, if one may so speak," his very next sentence
gives an idea of his commitment: "It is in quest of this surreality
that I am going, certain not to find it but too unmindful of my
death not to calculate to some slight degree the joys of its
possession" ("First Manifesto," 1981, p. 14).

The disagreement that arose between Miró and Breton, keeper
of the sacred flame and overseer of the orthodox Surrealists, over
these landscapes probably can be traced to that statement. If what
always mattered to Miró was reality, then he had nothing to do
with the dream. He may have set his imagination loose from its
moorings and shackles, but he did not paint his dreams. That task
he left to others, such as Salvador Dali. Miró was visual-minded; as
a painter, he measured his work with a yardstick calibrated
according to his own eye. Whatever confusion there may be resides
in the failure to distinguish between the two principles: the
imagination liberated and the dream crystallized. Fortunately,
protected by his tenacity and his decision not to communicate, Miró
did not fall into the trap of explanations and continued on his own
silent, anguished way: "I am tragical and taciturn by nature. Life
strikes me as absurd. It is not reasoning that shows me it as so:
I feel it that way, I am a pessimist" (to Yvon Taillandier, 1964).

It is in the nature of creation to proceed most often in a
disorderly manner. Themes pile up, to be forgotten, then return
and impose themselves on the artist's attention. Only a rare few

artists—Picasso, Klee, Léger perhaps—have worked in series in
which the works are linked to each other, which must be read in
succession, as a continuous entity, omitting nothing, in order to
discover and keep hold of the guiding thread and to learn how the
pictorial problems were approached, resolved, and then one day
abandoned.

Nude

Against a dark ground, two intersecting dotted lines dominate the
surface and divide it into four unequal zones (plate 91). The
vertical axis cuts across a strange white shape that looks drained of
blood, as if hanged. Around it, placed in a circle, gravitate forms,
clockwise from the top: blue green, white, yellow, red, and burnt
sienna; red orange and yellow; green and red; pale ocher. They
seem to be pasted on the surface, utterly flat, fixed yet somehow
fluctuating. Save for the leaf-fish, it would be risky to attribute a
precise name to them. Everything here is unstable, even if the clean
and neat contours suggest the contrary.

Are the axes meant as lines or dashes to direct our eye? The
other shapes—gentle undulations, curves, bulges, pure globes,
elongations—are all disposed with consummate skill. Yet the
picture seems to take its mystery from an incertitude on the edge
of formulation. Its construction may be precise, yet one can sense
an almost imperceptible tension, a displacement light as a feather's
touch. All these forms act as screens—they do not say what they
are and certainly not the opposite of what they wish to seem to be;
the opposition would be too harsh. They do not veil themselves but
simply evade our grasp. And to escape notice, they are prepared to
sink deep into the thickness of the night, there to play lascivious
and unpredictable games of hide-and-seek.

91. *Nude.* 1926. Oil on canvas, 36¼ × 28¾″ (92 × 73 cm). Philadelphia Museum of Art. Arensberg Collection

92. *Collage*. Summer 1929. Papier collé, 26 × 39⅜" (66 × 100 cm)

93. JAN STEEN: *The Cat's Dancing Lesson*. Oil on panel, 27 × 23¼" (68.5 × 59 cm). Rijksmuseum, Amsterdam

"I feel the need to attain the maximum of intensity with the minimum of means. This is what led me to give my painting a more and more stripped-down character.

"My tendency to pruning, to simplification, has come into play in three domains: modeling, colors, and the figuration of personages." —TO YVON TAILLANDIER

The series of paintings on white grounds, on whose objectively painted surface whimsical spots or broken lines are gracefully plotted, such as *The Firebird* (1927), would conclude with a veritable fanfare: the dazzling series of *Dutch Interiors* (1928; plates 94–102) and *Imaginary Portraits* (1929; plates 109–20).

When his life became a little easier, Miró seized the occasion to travel. The Low Countries—once ravaged by Spain—were only a few hours from Paris, and Flemish and Dutch paintings have always enjoyed an immense and legitimate prestige with the public and with official institutions. Although he took strong positions, Miró was no iconoclast: "I react magnificently to Poussin. And not to speak of Van Gogh, certainly, or Monet, who had already impressed me greatly in Barcelona. And obviously Goya, Greco...." (to Georges Raillard, 1977, p. 42). He reserved his disdain for conventional painting, the "oil-and-vinegar" variety, always made according to the same recipes, never upsetting anyone.

What he loved and wished to create was intensity. All his life he kept around him *xiurells*, the Majorcan folk whistles in white clay splattered with blue, yellow, red, and green spots, the colors he was so fond of: "Yes, the same colors, the primary colors, the pure colors, which contrast with each other" (to Georges Raillard, 1977, p. 90). Those implike figurines, whose ancestors are Phoenician and Greek with a touch of primitive sculpture, are modeled with the thumb. They reminded Miró of the enigmatic figures of the prehistoric cave painters; in fact, it was precisely in 1928 that he signed the provocative declaration that "painting has been in decadence since the age of the cave man." In a notebook of 1940–41, he wrote, "For *A Woman* think of the prehistoric idols reproduced in the first volume of the history of Spain owned by Alexandre" (Gaëtan Picon, *Carnets catalans*, 1976, Eng. ed., p. 129). "Folk art always moves me. There is neither cheating nor fakery in that art. It goes directly to the point. It surprises, and it is so very

rich in possibilities.... The older I grow, the more such art becomes important to me" (to Yvon Taillandier, 1964, p. 14).

Miró himself was about to push his audacity and his challenge to painting even further. This visual violence, this disorientation of the real—which he would challenge by using the painting of others as his point of departure, his springboard—had to find other means to express itself. The spirit of the time called for it. Partly out of curiosity, partly from the need to explore new domains, poets, like the painters, sought to make words and forms say something else than they had said in more or less the same manner for generations. They wanted to find another language, a new way to put words together. Poetry, painting, music no longer had rigid, precise frontiers; they seemed to have become porous, to let foreign influences infiltrate them.

Kandinsky and Klee conceived of painting as maintaining surprising relationships with music. Rilke, too, speculated about this new dispensation. In a letter to Méline of 23 February 1921, he poses the problem with regard to Klee's works. For Rilke, this was the most disturbing phenomenon of the day, although a liberating one. At this time, artists dreamed of a "total art." The famous utopian idea of the integration of the arts that was inherited from the Renaissance had never ceased to haunt certain minds. Only an opera, by the nature of its structure, might hope to realize this, but it remained still to be conceived and written. Delaunay proposed to unite architecture, painting, and sculpture, and in 1923 Baranoff-Rossiné was at work on a magical piano on which forms, sounds, and colors would fuse and correspond by simple pressure on the keys, an idea dating from the eighteenth century. The Futurist Russolo in his turn, in 1930, would invent the "Russolophone."

Dutch Interiors

As target for his new approach, Miró made an ideal choice in *The Cat's Dancing Lesson* by Jan Steen (plate 93). That Dutch genre painter (Leyden, 1623/26–1679) and tavern keeper, with the moralizing tendencies standard to his time, was both a gifted artist and a hypocrite. He served a straitlaced society, professing its

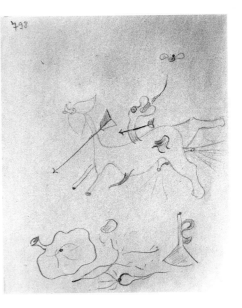

94, 95. Studies for *Dutch Interior II*. 1928. Pencil, both 8⅝ × 6⅝" (21.9 × 16.8 cm). Fundació Miró, Barcelona

respectability, with images it found pleasing; in turn, it willingly volunteered to serve him as model. If painting must be "assassinated," then Steen's would be the ideal victim. If one had to confront it with its opposite, it would be the art of the most ancient times, of the caves, when people could still express directly their fundamental drives: sex, hunger, death. Miró himself, unlike some of his Surrealist friends, who felt oppressed by conventions, had no intention of burning down the museums. What he wanted to do away with were pretty purrings, harmonious and cozy, convivial drinking songs, and to substitute savage dances around poetry, the unique and fatal woman to be snatched from the ashes.

There are three *Dutch Interiors* (plates 94–102), each preceded by important dossiers of studies, generally in pencil. With the very first drawing, the initial pretext is exploded. What was the point, then, in working from a picture postcard if nothing or practically nothing of it survives in Miró's extrapolations, unless it was used as a foil or contrast? At most, it would show what should not be done, what Miró was *not* after. In *Dutch Interior II* (plate 96), a simpering cat, a pitcher from a shipwreck, a guitar hanging from a nail, an animal closer to a farting jackass than a dog, a frying pan suddenly carrying on like an upside-down jug are all that survive of the little picture taken as pretext. Instead, there are flat shapes, cut out as if by scissors, against plain, flat grounds first divided into two large fields, dark and light, and then made uniform. They replace Jan Steen's protagonists, carefully positioned in the corner of a kitchen where they are making a cat dance on the table. No more illusionism, no more ribald and common allusions, no more hierarchies of the beautiful and the good—and, on the technical plane, no more modeling, perspective, natural light. These are replaced by red, white, blue, green patches that look like balloons suddenly released.

In *Dutch Interior I* (plate 102), a neatly drawn foot painted black and a triangle trying to pass itself off as a trowel declare themselves openly yet remain strangers, lost, separated by a whimsical tube connected to a tattooed white fire balloon seemingly suspended in space. *Dutch Interior III* (plate 98) has a black spot and a red spot locked in the circle of a serpent-arm that ends in a foot-hand with outspread fingers. "The serpent (?) harpooned with nails in the

first drawing—it also emerges from *Dutch Interior II*, the three *Interiors* having made a number of exchanges along the way—becomes the arm of a woman in childbirth, pierced by a monstrous nail" (Pierre Georgel, preface to *Dessins de Miró*, exhibition catalogue, 1978–79).

Still Life with Lamp

Still Life with Lamp (plate 106): a scarf of smoke, a dance of moths around what looks like a pigeon lamp set on a bare table. Even if the inventory numbers of the preparatory drawings do not reflect the order in which they were done, it is plausible, although not certain, that numbers 808 and 805 are closely related, probably made around the same time, while numbers 802, 807, and 809, devoted to a detailed study of the lamp, are most likely successive (plate 103). The theme of the moths (?) metamorphosing into embryos is worked out in number 804 (plate 104). A new condensed form—wing + insect + movement—is the ultimate metaphor leading, in number 803, to the definitive structure of the picture. The last, number 810 (plate 105), is simply the final state squared up for transfer.

A large, very smooth yellow plane (the table) and an agitated background (the wall) almost equally divide the surface. They are firmly fastened together by a long bar whose red shape organizes the space. The spiral topping it introduces the idea of the cylinder (baton). To left and right appear unstable forms suggesting very different movements: the globe where smoke is held in suspension brings to mind slow displacement; a hybrid insect (or gliding shadow), the frantic beating of wings. The elevated perspective, even where surreptitiously disavowed in the right half, is what gives the composition a magisterial authority. Static and dynamic confront each other.

The 1926–27 *Landscapes* (plates 86–91) and the *Dutch Interiors* (plates 94–102) brought into Miró's work a global vision in which, through the starry mirror of metaphor, objects are metamorphosed, in juggleries that foster poetic ambiguity and the upsurge of the unconscious. And the cone or pyramid (whichever name is used to

96. *Dutch Interior II.* 1928. Oil on canvas, 36¼ × 28¾″ (92 × 73 cm). The Peggy Guggenheim Collection, Venice

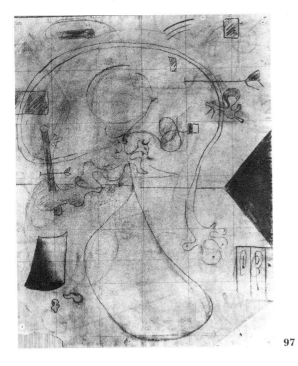

97

97, 99–101. Studies for *Dutch Interior III*. 1928. Pencil.
Fundació Miró, Barcelona

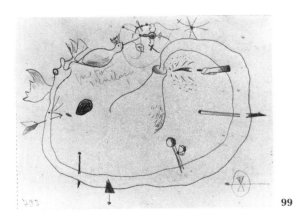

99

98. *Dutch Interior III*. 1928. Oil on canvas, 51⅛ × 37¾″
(130 × 96 cm). Private collection, Chicago

100

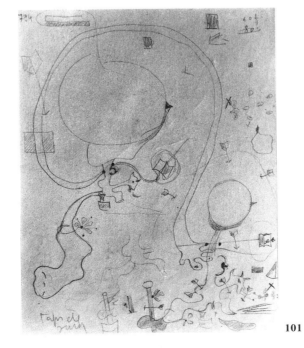

101

102. *Dutch Interior I.* 1928. Oil on canvas, 36⅛ × 28¾″ (92 × 73 cm). The Museum of Modern Art, New York. Mrs. Simon Guggenheim Fund

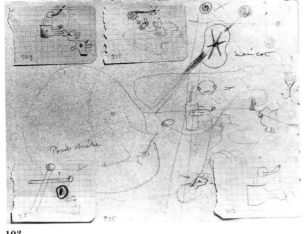

103

104

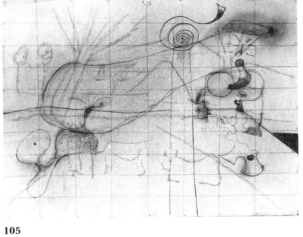

103–5. Studies for *Still Life with Lamp* (Nos. 805–9, 804, 810). 1928. Pencil. Fundació Miró, Barcelona

105

106. *Still Life with Lamp.* 1928. Oil on canvas, 35 × 44⅞″ (89 × 114 cm). Collection Mme. Marcel Duchamp

107. *Spanish Dancer.* 1928. Feather and hatpin on canvas, 39⅜ × 31½" (100 × 80 cm). Private collection, Paris

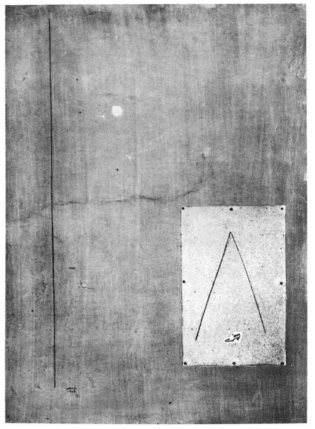

108. *Spanish Dancer.* 1928. Pasted papers, 41⅜ × 28¾" (105 × 73 cm). Private collection, Paris

label it), the spiral, the pierced disk, the glowing rod, the sparkling lamp—even if the artist has not used them for their symbolic value, they murmur what is not to be said. Reading *Still Life with Lamp* is a delight; the eye, intrigued at first, ends by surrendering to the surprises that await it, to the traps set for it.

Collages

In their famous collages, the Cubists Picasso, Braque, and Juan Gris had attempted a new definition of pictorial space. The Futurists tried to telescope space and time. Arp, Miró's friend and neighbor and a marvelous poet, experimented with cutout papers and exhibited the results in 1915. Sonia Delaunay had exploited the technique brilliantly, as early as 1912, as did Sophie Tauber-Arp, beginning in 1916. The first collages by the admirable Kurt Schwitters date from 1919. All of the Dadaists enthusiastically embraced the medium. To mention all those who at one time or another were intrigued by it would make too long a list, and in any case the approach now has become habitual, if not common.

Then, too, this was a time when the painter's eye was tending ever more to liberate itself from the constraint of a fixed point from which to observe and organize the world on the canvas through the artifice of perspective. The Cubists viewed objects from all sides in order to spread them on the surface. The Futurists sought to describe the trajectory of a body moving swiftly through space. By exploiting color contrasts, Robert Delaunay

opened painting to simultaneity. His masterly, intuitive work *Eiffel Tower* (1910) bears the dedication "...the tower addresses itself to the universe. Movement in depth...."

Everything was in movement. The era of the ephemeral—inaugurated by the Impressionists when they made a system out of the instability of light on objects in nature—had not yet run its course. In that grand caravan of shifting and changing ideas that marked the first decades of this century, as early as his first efforts at collage (plates 92, 107, 108), Miró took a stance of his own. His friendships among the Surrealists notwithstanding, he kept a respectful distance from their use of collage as vehicle of dreams and strange tales, and he removed himself entirely from the Cubists' "pasted papers," with their freight of overly intellectual speculations. Nonetheless, his own essays in collage—games on space—approached the Cubists' spatial explorations. Unlike them, however, he had little interest in the material used, was less concerned with its aesthetic aspects and deliberately more casual and unpolished.

On the other hand, his superpositions of planes and their interpenetration were skillfully carried through. They slide across each other or connect up with precision. However concise and decisive his idea, anything overly sharp is promptly corrected by a light, swift, sparing graphism. The line slips in and out, above, below, and hides only to reappear. It corrects what might be too dry in the shapes the scissors cut out or it leaves alone the unexpected effects of torn paper with its irregular contours. On these jagged edges, light catches and sparkles, now velvety, now brilliant, and captivates the eye. Without modeling or chiaroscuro, the smooth or irregular contour stands out against a uniform colored ground. In any case, Miró's taste and natural propensities inclined him toward montages of objects of different colors and materials. The result was no longer the monologue of a single material in its narrow register but popular dance music, gay or grave, in which all the instruments combine into a new and harsh harmony.

In 1930 Miró had another solo exhibition at the Galerie Pierre. The Valentine Galleries gave him his first exhibition in New York. He took part in the show of collages, in Paris (Galerie Pierre) and Brussels (Galerie Goemans), organized by the Brussels picture dealer Goemans. On that occasion, Louis Aragon wrote an important preface with the significant title "La Peinture au défi" (Painting challenged): "A manufactured object can perfectly well be incorporated into a picture, constitute in itself the picture. An electric globe becomes for Picabia a young girl. One sees that here the painters are beginning to truly make use of objects as words. . . . It is time moreover to understand that the hour has come when everything that passed as caprice in Ducasse's *Poésies* must be viewed as the prophetic expression of an upheaval of which we are the unseeing workers. . . . The modern collage requires our attention for what is deliberately intended in it and is absolutely opposable to painting, beyond painting" (Aragon, 1965, pp. 49, 53, 54).

If the champions of Surrealism had in mind to use collage in order to get rid of painting—the painting they judged without interest—for Miró, that kind of arrogant attack was beyond comprehension. He had only a single desire: to travel his own road, weathering its chaos, ruts, and storms and letting all such

skirmishes, excommunications, and exhortations pile up as litter in the ditches alongside; they meant nothing to him. His strength lay in his Catalan self-confidence and tenacity.

Queen Louise of Prussia

At the same time Miró was playing with superimposing or combining pieces of paper with their edges turned back like an animal's bared jaws, he was also painting *Imaginary Portraits*.

In its imperative structure, *Queen Louise of Prussia* (plates 109–11) is related to Miró's collages, with their clarity of design. The forms are sharply defined. The personage who has made her way slowly through numerous preparatory drawings stands out in silhouette against the background. The painting is articulated on a rhythm of cutout papers, sharp and percussive. Orange, yellow, brown, red, black, and a green border are brought out and made to vibrate by the blackness of the flaring skirt. The only disturbance in these carefully worked-out planes comes from the irregular brown quadrilateral, where the brush has worked the paint to leave in view a large darker curve. At the top of one drawing, Miró noted: "very concentrated/ the spirit pure/ no painting!" and then lower: "but *very rich* as color/ precious material/ very well painted." It happens that the hand and the mind may make demands to which the eye refuses to subordinate itself. Here, the space still belongs to painting, while the shapes could have been cut out of paper and pasted on the surface.

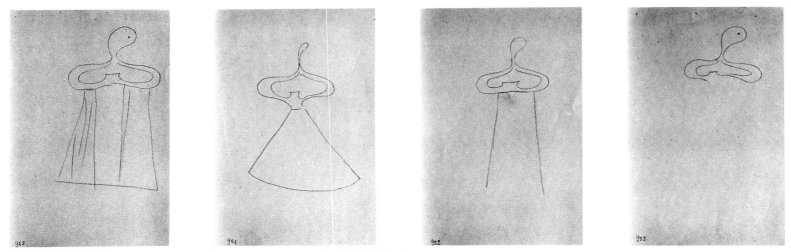

109, 110. Studies for *Queen Louise of Prussia*. 1929. Pencil. Fundació Miró, Barcelona

110

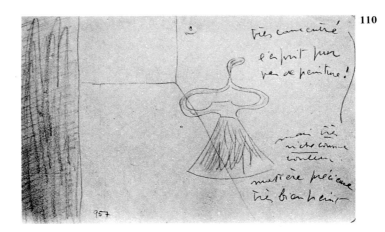

90

111. *Queen Louise of Prussia.* 1929. Oil on canvas, 31⅞ × 39⅜″ (81 × 100 cm). Meadows Museum, Dallas

112

113

114

115

112–17. Studies for *Portrait of a Lady in 1820*. 1929. Pencil. Fundació Miró, Barcelona

116

117

Portrait of a Lady in 1820

This time, Miró took on Constable, the precursor of Impressionism from whom Delacroix, in the hours immediately preceding the official vernissage, derived the background for his *Massacre at Chios* (1824).

From its English prototype, the "portrait" (plates 112–18) retains—with brilliant humor—no more than the five buttons on the bodice. The final image represents a lion and deliberate distillation of its model's form. Against a light yellow ground, the lady surges up, astonished, firm as a barricade, scissored out like a palm tree in a deep yellow. But for slight variations in color, the shapes seem cut out by a razor from a prepared paper, so precise is the separation between colors. In its course, the line shows very slight changes in direction, like the marks left by a hesitating hand cutting with a blade. Everything is flat, dry, hard, without volume, and the relationship between form and ground seems to belong to the world of pasted papers.

119. *La Fornarina*. After Raphael. 1929. Oil on canvas, 57⅛ × 44⅞″ (145 × 114 cm). Peril Foundation, Rydal, Pa.

120. Study for *La Fornarina*. 1929. Charcoal, 25¼ × 19⅜″ (64.1 × 49.3 cm). Fundació Miró, Barcelona

La Fornarina

If *La Fornarina* (after Raphael) (plates 119, 120) were not in fact the last of the *Imaginary Portraits*, it would still seem to culminate that adventure in which, contrary to Miró's forthrightly announced intentions, his painting profited by a purportedly illegitimate commerce with pasted papers. A black velvet mountain bears at its summit an enormous bust with breasts, arms, shoulders in a single mass, a mouth like a red boat, a perfect sphere from which escapes a fish-shaped eye, and all topped by a chocolate coiffure, hair and feathers admixed. A fabulous form cut out against a night-blue ground, it transfixes shadow. Here Miró's intention is even more applicable: "Precious material/ very well painted."

Visibly, Miró had been going through a difficult passage. Torn in contrary directions, puzzling over the path to choose, his own painting had to go through the experience of what has been called "antipainting." The very painting challenged by Miró's fellow-travelers itself picked up the gauntlet. Considering the course of Miró's work during those preceding six years, one can conclude with Jacques Lassaigne, "He disassembled the 'working parts' of living beings and things and, by depicting them with complete autonomy of means and rearranging them in a new order, invested them with a significance at once general and particular, and an evocative power like that of archetypal myths and esoteric figurations. Though no one had a clearer insight into the secrets of the natural world, Miró never became a slave to them, but used them as a means both to the exploration of the human psyche and to the expression of a cosmic imagery. And in doing so he clothed the imaginary with convincing form" (Lassaigne, 1963, p. 62; p. 62).

On 12 October 1929, Miró married Pilar Juncosa in Palma de Majorca and then moved back to Paris.

One may well ask if, by throwing the means of painting into question as he did in 1929, Miró did not trap himself in a blind alley, going too far in trying to reduce the art itself. For a painter to deny the powers of painting may be akin to denying himself. But then again, it may have been only that his creative energy was for the moment at low tide. For certain temperaments, personal happiness does not jibe with the need to create. Solitude interrupted and new satisfactions can throw an artist off his track. A happier life does not necessarily bring a fever of ideas. Creative ardor is often a compensation; solitude and work go hand in hand, pleasure and work more rarely. Work is often an excellent means of escaping from painful solitude, but even more often work rules out pleasure—unless, for the individual, they are one and the same. After so many years of struggle and deprivation, Miró may have found it difficult to regain his balance and powers of concentration when he became first a young husband and then a father. His merit was to have himself sensed the danger and, with a gardener's patience, waited for the season to turn. Instead of plowing the same furrow, he took to working with different materials, which helped him catch his breath and win back the old vigor of invention.

Objects and Constructions

Always the attentive gardener who knows how and where best to plant the seed, Miró once more found in what is inherent and symbolic in material itself the shift in focus necessary for a fresh outlook, for sowing a new crop. A flower, like the work of art, seems to appear suddenly one day, balancing gracefully on the end of its stem, yet it is the outcome of a prolonged cultivation, the gardener's attentive care more important, in the long run, than mere know-how.

In March 1931, Miró turned away from painting toward the *object* (plates 121, 122). This was not yet sculpture but simply a three-dimensional volume set against a flat picture surface to break it up, play with it. In organizing this surface, Miró was again plumbing space, but he was exploring it from a different tack. The constructions of 1930 are austere: ordinary planks of rough wood enhanced by a few nails, a shape cut out and painted, enlivened by the shadows it casts, which create illusory and changing forms. Here, Miró could utilize light, its movements, its changes. The ephemeral, a new element in his work, was seized on and utilized for itself. Something of the magic lantern was added to geometrical structure and made it more supple, vulnerable. Without light, the

work would close in on itself, keep its secret. Only under the effects of light does it reveal itself, open outward.

The exploration of the ephemeral was one of the great apprehensions of the Baroque. It undermines the very structure of a work by causing it to lose its essential character. One instant, the work changes into something else; the next instant, it has ceased to exist, because it is no longer what it had seemed to be and cannot pretend to be that thing when deprived of whatever that fleeting instant had brought to it. This idea, which began at the end of the sixteenth century as a theory and a way of conceiving the world, slowly penetrated the domain of art. The industrial development of the European societies and the acceleration and diversification of the means of communication helped to propagate it and encouraged its infiltration. New technical inventions in the first quarter of our century made the world smaller, and movement—by nature ephemeral—placed its mark on the sensibility of the age. In one way or another, all the new artistic approaches of the time integrated this idea into their particular expression, so much so that it would seem to be one of the key concepts transforming the artists' representation of the world.

Bricolage—puttering with all sorts of things, chiefly for the simple joy of working with one's hands—is the corollary to this concept of time. By its means, artists annexed new lands to exploit. Once judged unworthy of interest, now it demanded their attention. The first victims were the so-called noble materials: gold, marble, bronze, oil paints. Castoff objects, disfigured by the accidents of time, mutilated, in pieces, the refuse of everyday life suddenly became worthy of notice. To be taken into consideration, a bottle had no need to be dressed up as an elegant decanter; to be sculpted, a form no longer had to be cast in bronze or hewn from granite. Realizing the inherent provocation in every new idea, Marcel Duchamp titled a urinal *Fountain* (1917), and then he realized the ultimate in instability with, among other things, *Elevage de poussière* (Dust breeding) (1920).

Behind such manifestations, considered scandalous at the time, is the idea, at once poetic and magnanimous, that the artist's lightning-flash decision can change the way we all look at the world and (ambitiously, too ambitiously probably) can lead humankind to slough off the accumulations of habit and face up to the unknown, the revelation. From that point of view, in agreement with the physicists who explore reality, as well as the psychologists, one can say that things are not what they are but what we think they are. *Bricolage*—three-dimensional collaging, assemblage—is thus the triumph of the imagination. In the hands of an artist, whether

121. *Untitled.* 1931. Painted wood, cork, shell, and metal, 17¾ × 19⅝" (45 × 50 cm). Stedelijk Museum, Amsterdam

122. *Man and Woman.* March 1931. Oil on wood and metal elements, 13⅜ × 7⅛ × 2⅛" (34 × 18 × 5.5 cm). Private collection, Paris

123. ALEXANDER CALDER: *Female Dancer and Sphere.* 1936. Mobile, 21⅝ × 26 × 13¾" (55 × 66 × 35 cm). Galerie Maeght Lelong, Paris

guileless or perverse, there is no bottle fragment, tin can, snarl of rusted wire that cannot become something else: precious gems, a clamorous altar, hair with a Venetian glow. It was into this forbidden and marvelous no-man's-land that Miró was now about to venture, on tiptoe as usual, with due precaution and method.

Painting, however, intervened, still with its word to say. An ornament as regards color, it is also like a commentary. Even in a reduced role, it is a word, in its brilliance a note, a way to catch attention. Miró then proceeded by juxtaposing forms, and it is certainly this that earns his works a particular and unique place in the field of sculpture. The works are propositions, traps of contradictions; they remain invented objects, without utility. Everything can be wed—but not necessarily in a happy marriage. Wood cohabits with stone or iron; the ephemeral with the durable; feather or silk with some onetime but no longer useful object. A stuffed cockatoo becomes attached to a celluloid fish, a map of the heavens to a woman's slipper. A heavy chain, erotic instrument of fortune or slavery, is hung between two nails hammered into a wooden rectangle with painted decoration to become, in accordance with Miró's repeated phantasmic obsession, *Man and Woman* (1931; plate 122).

Ultimately, the unusualness of the fragment is what gives the

work pungency; a surprising extravagance leaves the viewer disoriented, in suspense. At the same time, while the difference in materials utilized plays an important part, all contribute to the effect of the whole. Objects that are dead, thrown away, part of the great moraine our society leaves on its course, take on life again as soon as someone has picked them out. In their assemblage, they become a protest against degradation, a defiance to oblivion—all good reasons to impel Miró to venture from the familiar medium of painting and deal with these objects, manipulating and reassembling them.

Following the example of Henri Focillon's admirable text about the hand, someday someone should write a praise of puttering. The objects saved from disaster hold tenaciously to life. Such manipulation of the imagination has profoundly influenced the plastic arts since the start of the century. Among much else, we owe to it the only original proposal to send sculpture in a new direction. Alexander Calder, an intimate friend of Miró since 1928, in his mobiles (plate 123) introduced movement as a means of defining volume and thereby transformed sculpture into something new: "One can say...that Calder sculpted movement rather than matter" (Gabrielle Buffet). Calder has always acknowledged his debt to Miró while adding, surprisingly, his gratitude to Mondrian.

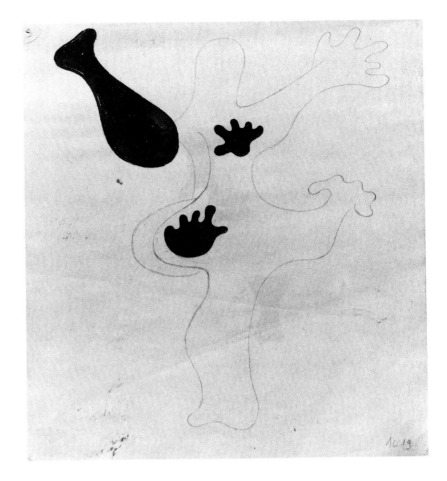

124, 125. Costume sketches for *Jeux d'enfants.* 1932. Pencil and gouache, 8⅛ × 7⅛″ (20.6 × 18.1 cm). Fundació Miró, Barcelona

Jeux d'enfants

Léonide Massine, choreographing for the Ballets Russes de Monte Carlo, invited Miró to create settings and costumes for a ballet, a proposal that came at a good moment. With scenario by Boris Kochno and music by Georges Bizet, the ballet, titled *Jeux d'enfants,* is a one-act divertissement evoking the pranks of toys that come alive at night and become swept up in a lively dance. Miró was expected not only to paint the stage curtains, as he had done for *Roméo et Juliette* in 1926, but to provide the entire décor (plates 124, 125). Massine knew Miró, and it was after seeing the painter's show of objects and painting-objects at the Galerie Pierre in December 1931 that he chose him for this task, as Dupin suggests. Massine himself has said, "Miró's art is very close to choreography: the extraordinary originality of the forms, their assurance in both drawing and volume, round out and aid the movement that goes on against them. Miró's colors are rich and, by the force of their harmony, give a spatial or plastic value to the dynamism of the choreography....Seeing the coordination of colors and forms in these pictures, one involuntarily feels a joy and a need to dance" (*Cahiers d'Art* 9, nos. 1–4, 1934, p. 50).

The back of the stage was enlivened by brightly colored broad stripes and completed by two large white and black geometrical forms, as well as mobile constructions that transformed the stage picture as required. The rocking horses, rackets, soap bubbles, bareback riders, sportsman, and traveler were dressed in "very stylized tights and tunics, with splashes of pure color and such simple motifs as hands" (Dupin, p. 248). The accessories were treated in the same manner, and with the lucid fantasy one would expect. Premiered on 14 April 1932, the ballet was a success in Monte Carlo as in Paris.

For Miró, the ballet gave him the opportunity to study the effect of forms and colors in a regular geometrical space, the horizontal oblong of the stage. He gauged well the resulting intensity, and, in addition, how forms and colors delineated that space, spread out in it, modified it, contrived to live in it. Certainly it was an instructive experience for him, creator of imaginary spaces.

This problem of the pictorial space led Miró to change repeatedly the terms of his investigations. He experimented even more often and modified the form of his questions in order to elicit different replies, which seem never to have satisfied him fully. He did this not from virtuosity, a quality he did not care for and which he reproved in Picasso, for one. Everything tells us that that was not what he was after. Instead, he was testing out the means of painting, tracking it down in all its haunts to make it show itself. Like a hunter, he lay in waiting, set his snares.

126. *The Twin Sisters in the Forest at Twilight.* June 1931. Oil on canvas

127. *Painting.* 1933. Oil on canvas, 51⅛ × 63¾″ (130 × 162 cm). Kunstmuseum, Bern

128. *Painting.* 1933. Oil on canvas, 51⅛ × 63¾″ (130 × 162 cm). Philadelphia Museum of Art. The A. E. Gallatin Collection

Large Paintings After Collages

From March to June 1933, Miró worked in Barcelona on a group of large and very beautiful canvases (plates 127, 128, 133). They were inspired by a series of highly fragmented and schematic collages, using among other things small printed vignettes, the pasted pieces almost lost in the opalescent immensity of a sheet of paper. These works preserve the precise cutout shapes of the small illustrations Miró took from tool catalogues, where they break up the surface of the light-colored page. Against bronzed bluish gray grounds, light and fluid and very delicately modulated, small bone shapes seem to swim in a limitless ether. Here and there, a graphic sign unobtrusively takes its place in otherwise empty areas. Sometimes, it may be barely noticed, but it succeeds nonetheless in implanting itself between the brightly colored patches and the picture ground, thus creating an intermediary localization, which accentuates the floating effect of the large shapes.

Those shapes, like the physicists' Cartesian diver in a flask, are suspended or glide about within a mysterious universe where, for a fraction of a second, their aimless course is arrested by a painter for whom the world manifests itself above all through its élan, its dynamic force. To translate movement, to pin down its traces on canvas or paper, has always been a torment for painters, because painting is static by definition and does not lend itself to such representation. Artists have invented numerous solutions, dating from the origin of time, to overcome the problem, and for centuries the metaphor offered at least the possibility of suggesting it. However, it was only toward the middle of our century, using ingenious or mechanical contrivances, that movement would finally be integrated into the colored work.

Personages in the Burnt-Down Forest, The Twin Sisters in the Forest at Twilight

The years 1930 and 1931 were marked by a few large canvases in which one senses a grimace more than uncertainty or awkwardness. The painter's heart was not in them, and he forced himself, by obligation. *Personages in the Burnt-Down Forest* (March 1931; plate 129) suffers from aridity. The forms are stiff, appliquéd. *The Twin Sisters in the Forest at Twilight* (June 1931; plate 126) lacks true spontaneity. Composition and forms are constrained; lines and painted surfaces open up to lifeless voids; any quiver of life is banished.

129. *Personages in the Burnt-Down Forest*. March 1931. Oil on canvas, 31⅞ × 39⅛″ (81 × 100 cm). Fundació Miró, Barcelona

130. *Man and Woman.* 1931. Oil on Ingres paper, 24¾ × 18⅛″
(63 × 46 cm). Private collection, United States

131. *A Woman.* 1932. Oil on panel, 18½ × 14⅝″ (47 × 37 cm).
Collection Kirk Douglas, Beverly Hills

Paintings on Ingres Paper

From 1931 to 1933, Miró experimented at length with painting on
Ingres paper (plate 130). Exploiting the whiteness of the sheet, he
laid on streaks of bright colors, often with a very broad brush. On
the ground thus created, he drew a black graphic sign, thick or airy,
which modified the density of the space. The independent line of
color enters into conflict with the graphic sign; as they are of equal
force, it provokes a tension that spreads across the entire surface.

Paintings on Panel

In the summer of 1932, once again in Montroig, Miró produced a
series of small wooden panels, paintings sparkling with color and
monumental in their forms yet realized with sheer delight in minute
detail (plates 131, 132). A shift in plane, generally effected by an
abrupt variation in color, plus a horizon line either high or low are
enough to define a visible space where female bodies rise up.
Painted one after the other, they obey a rhythm of an extraordinary
authority. Certainly, the disarticulation to which the painter subjects

these phallic women seems to arise from a violent motion. They
turn, gesticulate, bend, sit down, turn upside down. The painter
observes them from a precise point and notes the deformations that
evolution inflicts on them. The changes in planes accomplished by
color seize the forms moving on the surface, but without completely
upsetting their morphological coherence.

These are not imaginary creatures such as Miró had already
painted, nor human forms thrown into disorder and then
recomposed, but women deformed by wild movement, by an
ecstatic dance. Comparison with Picasso's *Woman in a Red Armchair*
of the same date shows how much Picasso reacted as a sculptor in
that work, making the form itself turn. Miró, however, faithful to
himself, lays his figures flat into a flat space suggested by color
alone; he was still mindful of the Catalan Romanesque frescoes.

He must have been satisfied with these small panels, because he
agreed to show them almost immediately, at the Galerie Pierre Colle
in Paris in December. The same year, Pierre Matisse, thenceforth
his correspondent in America, exhibited Miró's drawings and
paintings in his New York gallery.

132. *Flame in Space and Nude Woman.* 1932. Oil on panel, 16⅛ × 12⅝″ (41 × 32 cm). Fundació Miró, Barcelona

133. *Painting After a Collage.* 1933. Oil on canvas, 51⅛ × 63¾″ (130 × 162 cm). Fundació Miró, Barcelona

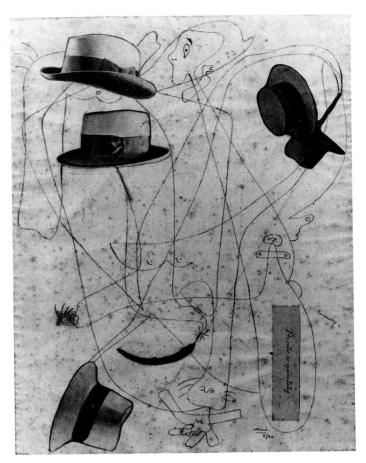

134. *Homage to Prats.* 1934. Conté crayon and collage on paper, 24¾ × 18½″ (63 × 47 cm). Fundació Miró, Barcelona

"The encounter between the instrument and the material produces a shock that is something living and which I think will have a repercussion on the viewers."
—TO YVON TAILLANDIER

Just as volcanic eruptions announce themselves in advance by throwing up rubble and vapors, so major events are preceded by rumors and disturbances. In 1931, a considerable part of the Spanish population refused to accept the break with the monarchy, and after the Republican electoral victory, the peninsula was cruelly divided. Beginning in 1934, the Asturian miners and the Catalan separatist movement were subjected to harsh social repression. Profoundly concerned, Miró watched the terrible succession of acts of violence which, with great ferocity, ended by setting Spaniard against Spaniard. As we know now, the fascists gained the upper hand.

Miró had always known which camp was his. In anguish, turning his back on the mastery he had attained, he hurled himself into the fray. In the years to come, all of his works would sound a vehement protest, so much the more terrible because, faced with such crushing imbecility, he choked with indignation, rage, impotence. In such circumstances, whatever arms a painter can throw into the balance weigh all too little; the general racket is too loud for his voice to be heard, let alone listened to. But Miró owed it to himself to cry out.

Tapestry Cartoons

After a series of very beautiful collages, of which the most celebrated is one dedicated to his old friend Joan Prats, a Barcelona hat maker (plate 134), Miró realized a group of large tapestry cartoons, which are also superb canvases. These have the same supple line and elongation of form so striking in his collages. While always remaining nimble, the line may run along playfully, dawdle, come to a stop before starting out again, stretch out. The visual role entrusted to photographs and postcards pasted on the paper in the collages is taken over in these cartoons by bold white surfaces, radiant in their brilliance and whiteness. More than simply a compositional element, they have the visual weight to carry an entire zone. Over very smooth, transparent, delicate ocher backgrounds, independent shapes in red, yellow, and black balance one another without effort, each carefully worked out in relation to its neighbors and to the voids to which they give meaning.

A harmonious graphism winds through the tapestry project titled *"Escargot, femme, fleur, étoile"* (Snail, woman, flower, star) (plate 140), drawn with ease and obvious pleasure as if by "a notary's clerk too lackadaisical to lift his pen" (Michel Butor, 1969, p. 36). Writing is also drawing, as Miró, both poet and graphic artist, likes to remind us. This garland of words written in holiday mood is an arabesque that belongs to painting. Or, in another reading: along with a sense of speed, the writing adds the sense and sound of language to the forms and colors of painting without touching or disturbing the language itself; on the contrary, it is enhanced. "But he has painted his title among the figures in a running hand that implies a certain swiftness and continuity of line quite unlike what happens with printed characters, gliding, skating (scratching of old pens on the frozen pond of sheets of paper), oozing, spinning out (oscillations of the brush furrowing the canvas, sea of oil) from one end of the

103

136. *Woman.* 1934. Pastel on velvet paper, 41¾ × 27⅝″ (106 × 70 cm). Philadelphia Museum of Art. Arensberg Collection

135. *Personage.* 1934. Charcoal, pastel, and pencil on pink velvet paper, 42⅛ × 28″ (107 × 71 cm). Fundació Miró, Barcelona

word to the other, but those words themselves he has connected by a veritable leash which catches our eye in its loops and prevents us from considering one without the other: it is a ski track down which we speed, passing indefinitely from snail to star and from woman to flower, lasso capturing the actors and sweeping them along in its gentle cyclone" (Butor, p. 34).

In all ages the artist has been interested in the support on which he works. Primitive people sculpted rock, painted on stone or rock shingle, bark, or fiber, worked wood and metal according to their metaphysics or the skills their society had acquired. In the West, where a certain confusion was introduced by aesthetics (even if the word dates only from the eighteenth century), artists in search of beauty made use of material whose essential property was, in principle, its indestructibility. The care taken to ensure a long life for the artwork is proof enough of how precious it was for the artist as well as the prince. It was unbearable to think that a human creation could die, disappear. From this springs the power of the artist, which political forces usually desire to repudiate.

In the history of ideas, it was necessary to rule out the aesthetic as chief criterion of artistic activity before art could accept nature's fragility and haphazardness. Like civilizations, art, too, is mortal. It fell to the Surrealists to accord supreme place to the fleeting instant, the sudden shock, without regard to the material used. If for them poetry's task was to give life, this implied no less that it dispensed death as well: the fatal instant. Without speaking of a cult

of the ephemeral—the characteristic and very essence of music and dance, for example—the instantaneous came to be sought after and even, through the creative process, absorbed into domains before then closed to it.

What stimulated Miró and sparked off the fruitful impact was the instant when his eye lighted on and took possession of a surface, whatever it might be: "It is the material that takes my interest more than the tool; I have a real feeling for the support" (to Georges Raillard, 1977, p. 121). This goes beyond a simple predilection; between Miró and materials there was a veritable love affair, for Miró, love at first sight—with all the physical, erotic, imaginative resonances that that implies.

Pastels on Velvet Paper

Velvet (flocked) paper is used most often in interior decoration. Soft to the eye and the touch, it has an aspect of imitating something else, which, without quite being disagreeable, nonetheless gives it a false note. It is rather more apt for making lamp shades— for which it is, in fact, used—than for painting. Yet Miró took to using it and even—height of redundancy—chose to work on it with pastels (plates 135, 136). From anyone but Miró one might fear the worst, with materials that so lend themselves to pretty watered effects and the charming glimmer of butterfly wings. But Miró treated pastel with refinement, and the color transitions, so facile

138. *Painting.* Summer 1936. Oil, casein, tar, and sand on Masonite, 30¾ × 42½″ (78 × 108 cm)

137. *Painting.* 1934. Painting-collage on sandpaper, 14⅝ × 9½″ (37 × 24 cm). Philadelphia Museum of Art. The A. E. Gallatin Collection

139. *The Farmers' Meal.* 3 March 1935. Oil on cardboard, 29½ × 41¾″ (75 × 106 cm). Private collection, Cincinnati

with this medium, are made soberly and with a lovely subtlety. That sugary savor, however, which Miró succeeded in turning bitter as gall, helped to bring out from the velvety ground terrifying personages, women, creatures, forms half-insect and half-flab, grimacing swollen protozoans armed with sharp tusks, bellies heavy with phantasmic sex. Rounded shapes, under a glaucous light they growl, snigger; they seize the entire surface, heads in the stars, scraping their scales, clacking their thorns. With his crayons, Miró dug into the velvet, furrowed and gnashed the tender epidermis. He made it vomit, this cloyingly rich velvet paper, with the syrupy pastels that he considered the perfect choice to represent those mediocre people, everywhere in their place and in place everywhere, that he detested. Here, he attacked them with their own weapons.

Paintings on Sandpaper

Miró's choice of materials in this period is not explained solely by his professed taste for unusual supports. He took sandpaper, the kind that scratches and sparkles, and covered it with long, somber, stretched-out forms resembling human members, arms or legs ripped off and tossed about (plate 137). It was derisively that Miró confided to sandpaper images evoking fragility, oblivion: bruised and battered figures, signs in disequilibrium that the first puff of wind would blow away.

Paintings with Rope

The rope surrounded by personages grimacing in pain (plate 146) makes one think of the rope hanging in the barn that is used for other purposes, and which bivouacking soldiers make use of for their hasty business in the chill of early morning.

Paintings on Masonite

With continuing interest in rough boards, during the summer of 1936 Miró painted on panels of Masonite (plate 138), a construction material made of wood tar and sand mixed. On it, he utilized a casein paint, a risky material because it is crumbly, chalky, and adheres badly to the support, as if he had to express with his own hands the risk of destruction. To be active, to benumb himself with work, to busy himself without hope while accepting that he would see everything around him putrefy seemed to him the only possible way to silence his anguish.

The Farmers' Meal

In *The Farmers' Meal* of 1935 (plate 139), Miró returned to a theme dealt with in 1925. All his old world of feeling was summoned up here: the clock stopped at the hour of siesta, the cock, the blazing

140. Tapestry cartoon: *"Escargot, Femme, Fleur, Étoile."* 1934. Oil on canvas, 76¾ × 67¾" (195 × 172 cm). Fundació Miró, Barcelona

141. *Nocturne.* 9–16 November 1935. Oil on copper, 16½ × 11¾″ (42 × 30 cm). Private collection, Great Britain

142. *Seated Personages.* 10–21 March 1936. Oil on copper, 17⅜ × 13¾" (44 × 35 cm)

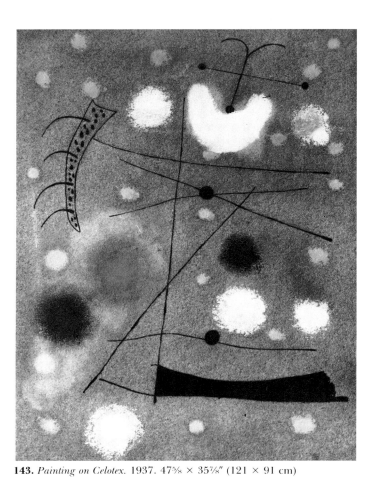

143. *Painting on Celotex.* 1937. 47⅝ × 35⅞" (121 × 91 cm)

144. *Painting on Celotex.* 1937. 47⅝ × 35⅞" (121 × 91 cm)

sun sitting on a table, the Catalan peasant big as a carnival procession giant, with pipe and jug in hand. But copulating dogs howl like the cry of death, and the hugely oversized head of an old corrida nag destined for the horn of a furious bull looms in the foreground. Its eye glassy, its ears daubed with paint, it chews on both the sugary carob bean and the bitter pill of disapproval, the one to help the other go down.

Paintings on Copper Panels

Miró also covered small, shiny copper panels with acid colors, mountainous and monstrous landscapes, men, women, giraffes, pitiable puppets, impotent actors in a sinister story (plates 141, 142, 145). Their figures are caught in the gangue of pictorial grounds worked painfully by a heavy brush, like cadavers buried under the ash spewed out by a volcano.

Paintings on Celotex

The paintings of 1937 on Celotex (plates 143, 144) function as a kind of musical pause. The sign disengages itself with difficulty from the colored mass hemming it in on all sides, a sea of sand in which it risks being engulfed. Although the line is clutched here and there by points of color hindering its progress, it pursues its dogged course.

145. *Man and Woman in Front of a Pile of Excrement.* 1935. Oil on copper, 9 × 12⅝″ (23 × 32 cm). Fundació Miró, Barcelona

146. *Rope and People I.* 27 March 1935. Oil and rope on cardboard mounted on wood, 41¼ × 29⅜″ (105 × 74.5 cm). The Museum of Modern Art, New York

147. *Still Life with Old Shoe.* 24 January–29 May 1937. Oil on canvas, 32¼ × 46″ (82 × 117 cm). The Museum of Modern Art, New York. Gift of James Thrall Soby

148. *"L'Été."* 1937. Brush and India ink,
15⅜ × 12½" (39 × 31.6 cm).
Fundació Miró, Barcelona

Still Life with Old Shoe

After all his growling at the state of the world and his vigorous protest of the imagination as a way of shaking off his distress, one might think that Miró needed a moment in which to resume contact with everyday things, with the quiet life. Indeed, he later described this as a period in which he needed to check everything against reality. Miró began *Still Life with Old Shoe* (plate 147) in Pierre Loeb's apartment and then continued working on it in his studio for some months, as indicated by the dates in his signature: 24 January–29 May 1937. Doubtless, he felt a need to have under his eyes objects like this old shoe, which may well call to mind Van Gogh's heartbreakingly sad hobnailed boots.

In a way, such real-life objects were perceived as protection against a fever always on the edge of breaking out. But such a guardrail, like all those preventive measures, was in fact neither very solid nor very effective, for what he sets before us is not a still life but, plainly and simply, a cataclysm. Reds, blues, greens, yellows, the colors of fire, illuminate with tragic flickerings the bottle melting under the heat, while the shoe itself is a drifting pan of burning coals. The wind piles up thick clouds of acrid smoke so dark, so opaque, so hard that they become the jaws of a vise. That piece of bread takes on the likeness of a death's-head, that fork impaling an apple with such force as to burst it open is a murder in the making. Despite its apparently modest pretext, this canvas is a metaphor of the horrors of war. It is clamor, indignation; it summons up all the artist's rage against the absurdity of the human condition.

Life Drawings at the Grande Chaumière

In the drawings Miró did from life in 1937 at the Académie de la Grande Chaumière (plates 149–51), the all-dominant line may glide smoothly and the arabesque twine majestically, but those male and female nudes with flaccid limbs, spatulate fingers, minuscule or contorted heads are adumbrations of human creatures deformed by disgust. A camera-like viewing angle elongates the proportions and modifies the model's appearance to become a type between animal and human: how much could irony serve as a recourse against a horror that every day grew more immediate?

Nude Ascending a Staircase (plate 151), which mockers set in opposition to Marcel Duchamp's *Nude Descending a Staircase No. 2* of 1912, is an atrocious caricature of woman beladen with all the hatreds Miró projected on her. In *"L'Été"* (Summer) (plate 148), he flings woman into a circle bristling with thorns, where she is "burned by the flames of the sun." The apparent calm of the composition and the signs renders more insidious the terror the artist feels at "the needles of her breasts," more miserable that "white and pink smile" her breasts address to the "crescent of the moon."

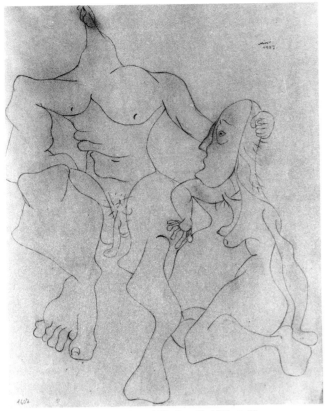

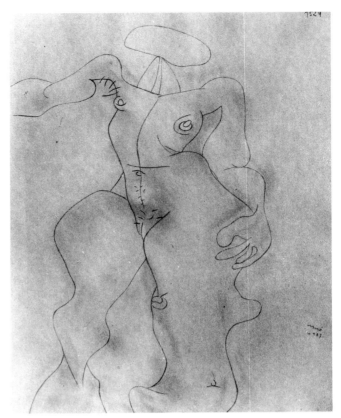

149. *Male and Female Nudes.* 1937. Pencil, 12¼ × 9"
(31 × 23 cm). Fundació Miró, Barcelona

150. *Female Nude.* 1937. Pencil, 10⅝ × 8¼" (27 × 20.8 cm).
Fundació Miró, Barcelona

The War in Spain

At five in the afternoon—*cinco de la tarde*—death entered the
bullring. When Calvo Sotelo, head of the monarchist party, was
assassinated on 13 July 1936, the army chiefs based in Spanish
Morocco, headed by General Franco, openly revolted, beginning the
Spanish Civil War on 18 July 1936. The shadow of death came to
loom over Montroig, Joan Miró's true and only homeland. From
that point on, it prowled around Miró, and he girded himself
against it.

To make oneself understood, one must sometimes regress to an
old, familiar path. All in the urgent desire to make himself
understood, Miró used every device at hand: he returned to the
modeling of his forms, to effects of perspective, to the norms, the
commonplaces, the formulas of accepted communication. An
expression of horror cannot be encumbered with style; it calls for
the words and customs of the tribe. But when horror explodes,
what need of polished language, of poetical subtleties? Miró had
painted on copper, used dark tar, rasping sand, materials that
scratch. With an old shoe and a gin bottle (plate 147) he had
denounced the firebrands of war, and his colors been made to
cry, "*Fire!*"

The Paris World's Fair of 1937 gave Miró the opportunity to cry
out his indignation publicly in a huge wall painting in the
Republican Spanish pavilion (plate 153). On an immense panel, his
Catalan peasant, armed with no more than a sickle, threatened the
airplanes sent by Hitler to machine-gun the population of a small
country town, caught unawares on a market day. Titled *The Reaper*,
in a clear allusion to death, the hideous figure makes itself heard
in an abject cry, whistling between rotted teeth. If the personage is

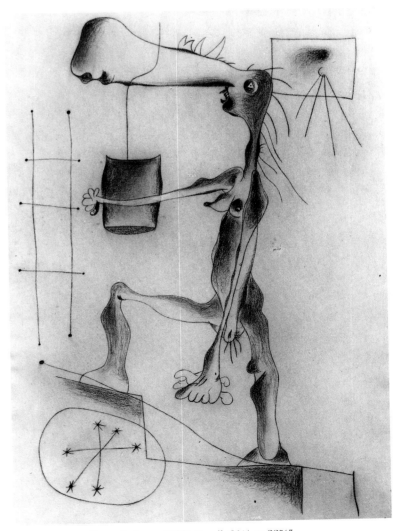

151. *Nude Ascending a Staircase.* 1937. Pencil, 31½ × 22⅞"
(80 × 58 cm). Fundació Miró, Barcelona

113

152. Project for a stenciled poster: *"Aidez l'Espagne."* 1937. 9¾ × 7⅝" (25 × 19 cm)

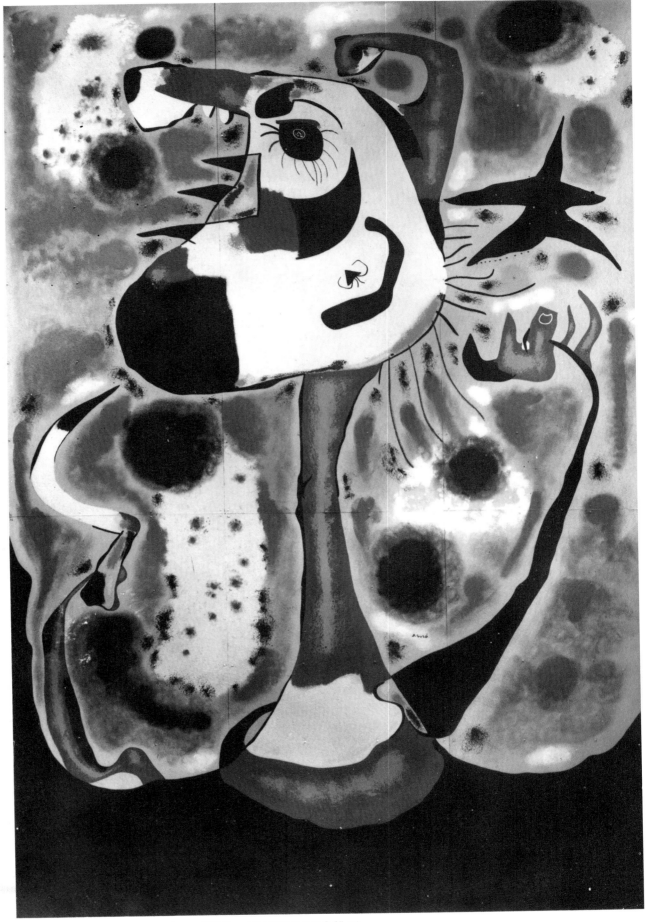

153. *The Reaper.* 1937. Oil on Celotex, 18'1½" × 11'11¾" (5.5 × 3.65 m).
Mural painting for the Spanish Republican pavilion, Paris World's Fair, 1937, lost

154. *Woman's Head.* 5 October 1938. Oil on canvas, 18⅛ × 21⅝″ (46 × 55 cm). Private collection, Los Angeles

indeed meant to be the image of death, the fact that he is brandishing not a scythe but a sickle, the Communist Party emblem, may indicate that Miró's unconscious made him disclose what officially he did not wish to say. The Surrealists, it should be kept in mind, were politically committed in that direction until they finally broke with the Communists in 1935. Miró, unlike Picasso, Aragon, Éluard, and Péret, never adhered to that party, nor did his political attitude ever bring him under the banner of any other group.

Miró also stenciled a poster, with brilliant colors against an ultramarine ground, calling for aid to Republican Spain (plate 152). He commented, "In the present struggle, I see old outworn forces on the fascist side, on the other side, the people, whose immense creative resources will give Spain an impetus that will astound the world" (*Cahiers d'Art* 12, nos. 4–5, 1937).

"I remember that period very well, that of fascism. I took refuge here in Palma and said to myself: 'Old man, you're done for! You're going to bed down on the beach and draw in the sand with a walking stick. Or else you'll be making drawings with the smoke of a cigarette.... You won't be able to do anything else, the game's up!' I had that impression clearly, at the time of Hitler and

Franco. Total block" (to Georges Raillard, 1977, p. 75).

The Reaper had its pendant in the no less horrible *Woman's Head* (1938; plate 154), the portrait of a witch, another likeness of woman as Miró imagined her, lacerated by her as much as he himself was bent on lacerating her. No defense could be too cruel against this abominable Ubuesque virago with horned beak and ulcerated teeth. This woman he sees as a universe is meant perhaps more directly as the universe itself in all its horror.

The Object of Sunset

Abruptly putting aside all preoccupation with painting, sculpture, art, and artifice, Miró produced a painting-object he titled *The Object of Sunset* (plate 156).

To this severed and mutilated penis, cut out of the trunk of a carob (the tree sacred to Montroig), he disconcertingly gave also a vagina spread open as if to whelp nihility. This chopping block is topped by a tired old bedspring, a kitchen-stove burner (resembling both man and target), a mooring hook, and the chain from a feeding trough. The paltry, mutilated objects grouped here, each fraught with the weightiest symbolic significances, become by no more than their mere presence as horrible as what they are meant to challenge: the war. Miró the poet, artist, man of profound culture succeeded for an instant in obliterating it all from his memory in order to become one with the brutal fact through this *Objet du couchant*, with its implication, in French, of the sun lying down *(se coucher)* to die. Of all his Surrealist fantasies, none is more alien to aesthetic and artistic considerations. It was received with general incomprehension, and André Breton deserves credit for having immediately grasped its sheer audacity and for having had the foresight to preserve it in his own collection. This is, effectively, the most *intolerable* of "objects."

Ironically, today it figures in the collections of the Musée Nationale d'Art Moderne, Paris, inventory number AM 1975–56, and is indicated in the catalogue as representative of a style and a period: "Surrealist sculpture-object." When that noble institution acquired it, Miró pointed out, "I want to make it clear to you, and this is of great importance, that [when] I light on anything whatsoever it is always by a magnetic force stronger than myself that I am drawn to it and fascinated."

155. *Poetic Object.* 1936. Construction of hollowed wooden post, stuffed parrot on wooden stand, hat, and map, 31⅞ × 12 × 10¼″ (81 × 30.5 × 26 cm). The Museum of Modern Art, New York

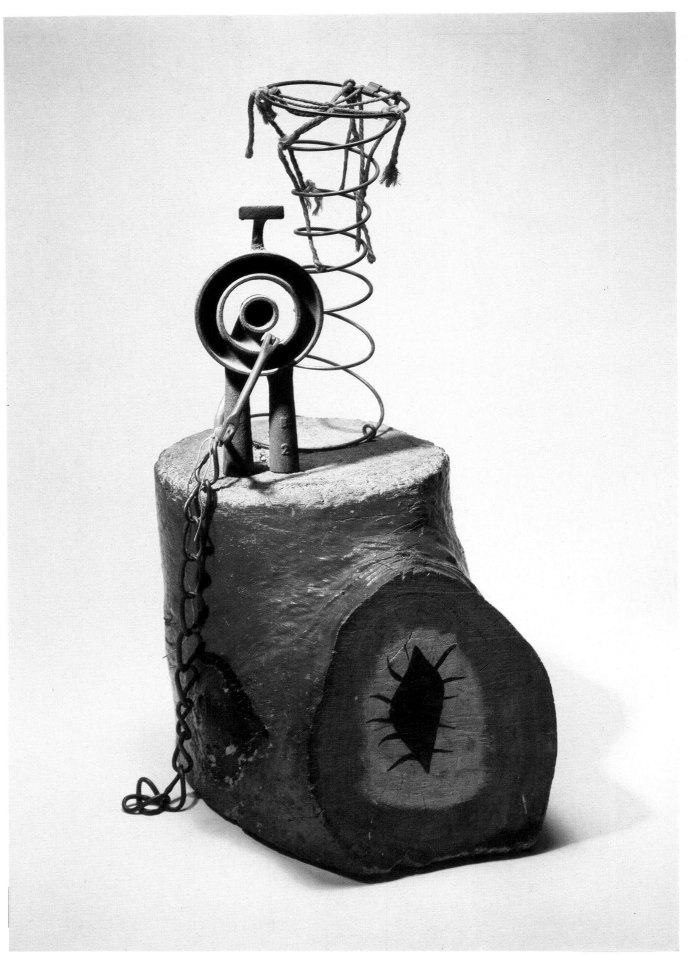

156. *The Object of Sunset.* 1938. Painting-object, 26¾ × 17⅜ × 10¼″ (68 × 44 × 26 cm).
Musée National d'Art Moderne, Centre Georges Pompidou, Paris

157. *Nocturnal Bird.* 30 August 1939. Oil on canvas, 16⅛ × 10⅝"
(41 × 27 cm)

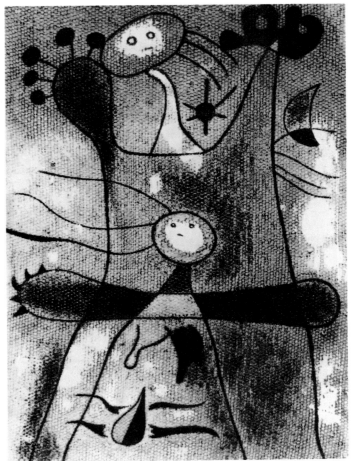

158. *Two Women.* November 1939. Oil on canvas. 21⅝ × 15"
(55 × 38 cm)

"What I desire is mental tension. But in my opinion, it is of prime importance not to provoke that tension by chemical means, such as drink or drugs.

"The atmosphere favorable to that tension I find in poetry, music, architecture—Gaudí, for example, is fantastic—in my daily walks, in certain noises: the noise of horses out in the country, the creaking of the wooden wheels of carts, footsteps, cries in the night, crickets."—TO YVON TAILLANDIER

War was declared, events moved swiftly in France. Everyone buzzed with questions; Paris was emptying. Each day brought its piece of bad news. The moment came when Miró was advised to leave the capital. The architect Paul Nelson, his friend, invited him to his house at Varengeville in Normandy.

Although his mind was troubled and his heart heavy, Miró discovered an entirely new landscape there. He was struck by the heavy flight of crows flapping their wings strenuously to remove themselves from the path of an oncoming train. This opulent nature, so verdant, so gently undulating, differed so greatly from his own familiar countryside that he found it strange. He discovered vast silken, moist skies and a silvery light that shattered into a thousand splinters on the angry sea at the foot of the chalk cliffs. Everything was new to him, everything the occasion for unanticipated exploration: the squalls of wind whistling across the moors; the skies one moment tormented, then shot through with stars and traversed by the great migrations of the clouds; the milky immensity; the triangular reflections of the water to the distant dim horizon—all this so opposite to the fantastic nature of his harsh land of Montroig.

Miró quickly set to work, turning out a few canvases with red grounds (plates 157, 158). These were followed by roughly painted works on wide-meshed, coarse-surfaced sacking, on which the brush catches, scrapes, wears away as it lays on its load of color and releases crabbed personages and stiletto-pointed stars from the bristly hemp. In future decades, certain American artists and critics would take the works of this time as obligatory points of reference for their own creative undertakings.

Some commentators believe that the famous series of *Constellations* (plates 159–67) was suggested to Miró by the new beauty of the region where he had taken refuge. They hold that the furious sea and dramatic sky aroused in him a cosmic fervor. Miró later assured his first biographer, James Johnson Sweeney, that the gouaches were inspired by "reflections in water. Not naturalistically —or objectively—to be sure. But forms suggested by such reflections" (Sweeney, 1948, p. 211).

For my part, I think these *Constellations* owe even more to the artist's overwhelming desire to forget the world and its terrifying threats. He had to escape into a pursuit that absorbed all his faculties, all his attention, all his willpower. His dancing and marvelous gouaches acted as a screen between himself and the world, a flight from fact. To Sweeney he later confided, "I felt a deep desire to escape. I closed myself within myself purposely" (Sweeney, p. 210). He nourished this profound need by listening to music in the night hours until his mind was numbed, by gazing at stars until his eyes swam. He had always loved music, and throughout his life he listened to it as he worked. It is not irrelevant

159. Study for *Constellations*. 7 September 1940. Pencil, 12⅜ × 9¼" (31.3 × 23.5 cm). Fundació Miró, Barcelona

that in this period he felt very close to the compositions of Bach and Mozart, which he regarded not as mere melodious accompaniment for his hours of melancholy and insecurity but as exemplars and models for him. From Bach he seems to have taken the admirable cadence and flawless mathematics, from Mozart the uncompromising tension beneath an apparent lightness and the rigor of motifs beneath the smooth stream of notes. Suggestions of Bach's *Goldberg Variations* and *A Musical Offering* and Mozart's *The Magic Flute* filter through the twenty-three gouaches Miró worked at untiringly and continuously for two years.

The problem Miró set himself in these gouaches called for delicate solutions, a balancing act achieved through his profound disposition and firm concentration, terms he himself used in speaking of these works. When one thinks of the hazards of the time and the sudden interruptions in his work brought on by the events of the day, it seems miraculous that he carried through this undertaking with no apparent sign of weariness or fatigue. These gouaches seem to have welled forth with utter freshness from his mind and brush. The idea was formulated in a few drawings (plate 159), as if Miró stealthily advanced upon something that was both trap and lure, something that would seize him and not let go until the exhausted prey surrendered—just when the cycle closes, ending at the same point where it had begun.

As the German troops approached and the bombings increased, Miró first tried unsuccessfully to get passage to America and then, on sober reflection, decided to return to Spain. That journey, with its many hazards, remained engraved on his memory; thanks to the liberal understanding of the Spanish consul in Perpignan, he reached his destination without too many problems. The return to fascist Spain has sometimes been held against Miró: " 'I thought a lot about that reproach which in fact was made against me, but kept to my original idea, which was that I had to remain on my Catalan earth.' (Here he stamped on the ground.) 'I felt the tragedy experienced by my comrades who had not returned to Spain, who were exiled, a personal tragedy but which has marked their work' " (to Georges Raillard, 1977, p. 31). It was at home again, in Montroig, that he completed the *Constellations*. For a time, he and his family lived in Barcelona, but even though the government chose the tactic of ignoring him completely—indeed, even acting as if he had never existed—life was difficult for them. The atmosphere was heavy, perhaps even threatening. To break loose, he moved to the island of Majorca, to Palma, home of his mother's family, where his eccentric grandfather José Ferra, a character out of an adventure story with an eternal love for great voyages, had finally settled down as a cabinetmaker. Shut off on his island, isolated, remote from the noisy outside world, Miró increasingly gave himself to meditation in the years to come.

The Constellations

These twenty-three works (plates 159–67) in gouache and oil wash on paper, realized between 21 January 1940 and 12 September 1941, present themselves as an uninterrupted network of intimately

160. *Constellation: The Escape Ladder.* Varengeville, 31 January 1940. Gouache and oil wash on paper, 15 × 18⅛″ (38 × 46 cm). Private collection, New York

related signs, each of which can be inferred from the other, that entangle themselves in a constantly renewed rhythm, in an unfailingly sustained tonality that is always of equal density. It was intelligent and perceptive of Pierre Matisse, after showing them in New York in 1945, where they were properly received and appreciated, to have them reproduced in a portfolio where the eye could study them as a totality and follow their development step by step. The inevitable but regrettable dispersal of the originals among various owners breaks the harmony and unity of a work in which each element is a star and the whole sets before us the self-contained system of a constellation.

The picture grounds, with their marvelous subtlety obtained by the freest of means—scraping, moistening, rubbing, polishing—in themselves constitute a spatial mystery. With their velvety blues, all degrees of white, every nuance of gray, they sound and vibrate like a note struck lightly yet firmly, seeming to invoke the appearance of the signs. Miró's entire world rises into view: curves, broken lines, points minute as a flower seed or dilated like the pupil of a cat, exclamation marks, colons, commas, double-feathered arrows, hearts, eyes, wolf's fangs, tiny gnomes sporting the Catalan peasant's red *baretina*, hourglasses distilling the measure, somnolent suns, crescent moons, great lemon-colored fiery tresses of comets, ultramarine blue oscillations of celestial bodies, stars, sexual parts. Like Cornelius Agrippa—philosopher-adventurer, scientist, mercenary in the armies of Maximilian of Austria and under other flags as well, wandering from one university town to the next in France and Italy and accused here and there of heresy and black magic—Miró seemed to want to write a new *De Occulta Philosophia* (1531), like the one in which that Renaissance surrealist claimed to be able to decipher in the trajectories of the stars, galaxies, and planets a nonhuman handwriting of surprising graphic character that marked the world below with celestial signs.

Although André Breton had reservations about Miró's work, detecting in it "a partially arrested development at the infantile stage which has left him ill-protected against unevenness, over-production and playfulness, and has set limits, intellectually, to the scope of his testimony" (Breton, 1965, p. 70; p. 70), in 1959, at Pierre Matisse's request, he wrote a series of very beautiful texts to accompany the reunited gouaches (one of which had disappeared in the meantime). In his preface, Breton declares, "They participate in and yet differ from each other in the manner of bodies in the aromatic and cyclic series in chemistry; considered simultaneously, both in succession and as a whole, each of them takes on the necessity and value of a member in a mathematical series; finally, the sense they convey of unbroken, continuous achievement at the highest level includes, in the term 'series,' as applied to them, the meaning it takes on in games of skill or chance" (Pierre Matisse

Gallery, New York, *Constellations*, 1959, exhibition catalogue, p. 5).

With respect to those complex relationships between painting and poetry that meant so much to Miró, it seems of interest to attempt a new parallel with Stéphane Mallarmé, a poet Miró professed to admire and who won Breton's approval as well. In a letter written in Besançon on 5 December 1866 to François Coppée, thanking that poet for sending him his volume *Le Reliquaire*, Mallarmé wrote, "Chance does not bring about a line of poetry, that is what matters. We have, several of us, achieved that, and I believe that, once the lines are so perfectly delimited, what we should aim at above all is that, in the poem, the words—which themselves already suffice to no longer receive impressions from outside—should reflect each other until they appear no longer to have a color of their own but to be only transitions on a scale. While there is no space between them, and although they fit together marvelously well, I think that sometimes your words live a little too much their own life, like the stones in a mosaic of jewels" (Stéphane Mallarmé, *Propos sur la poésie*, Paris: Éditions du Rocher, p. 85).

The apposition of these quotations from Breton and Mallarmé lets us see, among other things, through the notion of chance, which is keenly deplored and rejected by one, desired and respected by the other, why Breton was first drawn to Mallarmé and then rejected him. That contradiction was fundamental to Surrealism, decisive in that it above all calls into question the meaning of the poetic act. Further, Mallarmé's opinion casts light on the relationship, so difficult to pin down, between painting and poetry. It suffices to replace *words* by *signs* to make it evident that the "transitions on a scale" and the reflection of one on the other constitute a tension common to both poetry and painting, to poet and painter alike, and which Miró must have experienced just when he was working at his *Constellations*.

After the concentration, even asceticism, demanded by the *Constellations*, in which he broke with a painting of insurrection and cruelty, Miró had a real need to find his own bearings again. He told James Johnson Sweeney, "After lunch each day I would go to the cathedral to listen to the organ rehearsal. I would sit there in that empty gothic interior daydreaming, conjuring up forms. The light poured into the gloom through the stained-glass windows in an orange flame. The cathedral seemed always empty at those hours. The organ music and the light filtering through the stained-glass windows to the interior gloom suggested forms to me. I saw practically no one all those months. But I was enormously enriched during this period of solitude" (Sweeney, 1948, p. 211).

Considering the demands that the *Constellations* had made, it was natural that any new departure should still be imprinted with memories of that series, although here they are reworked, further developed, and transformed.

161. *Constellation: Awakening in the Early Morning.* Palma, 27 January 1941. Gouache and oil wash on paper, 18⅛ × 15″ (46 × 38 cm). Private collection, New York

162. *Constellation: Personages in the Night Guided by the Phosphorescent Tracks of Snails.* Varengeville, 12 February 1940. Gouache and oil wash on paper, 15 × 18⅛″ (38 × 46 cm).
Philadelphia Museum of Art. Louis E. Stern Collection

164. *Constellation: On the 13th, the Ladder Brushed the Firmament.* Palma, 14 October 1940. Gouache and oil wash on paper, 18⅛ × 15″ (46 × 38 cm). Private collection, United States

163. *Constellation: Toward the Rainbow.* Palma, 11 March 1941. Gouache and oil wash on paper, 18⅛ × 15″ (46 × 38 cm). Collection Mrs. Patricia Matisse, New York

165. *Constellation: The Migratory Bird.* Palma, 26 May 1941. Gouache and oil wash on paper, 18⅛ × 15″ (46 × 38 cm). Pierre Matisse Gallery, New York

167. *Constellation: Morning Star.* Varengeville, 16 March 1940. Gouache and oil wash on paper, 15 × 18⅛″ (38 × 46 cm). Private collection, Paris

168. *Personages in the Rain.* 31 August 1942. Brush and India ink, charcoal, watercolor, and pastel, 16⅝ × 30¼″ (42.2 × 77 cm). Fundació Miró, Barcelona

Gouaches, Watercolors, Drawings

For a time, Miró abandoned oil painting in favor of charcoal, pencil, pastels, and India ink with either brush or pen. These large drawings on canvas or paper (plates 168–76), both of which drank in the ink, are characterized by spiky lines, delicate spots, crackling or suspended signs, and bursts of color giving life to an entire population of vibrating women gazing at the sun or frightened by the night, of bogeymen among the stars welcoming the birds, of little hobgoblins pinching their noses, playing with question marks, chasing insolent commas, tracking down virulent mosquitos. To soothe his solitude, Miró would people it. He never tired of inventing, amassing stories, provoking on paper fabulous encounters no sooner limned than forgotten for new ones.

Like the Pied Piper of Hamelin, attracting rats to him by the sound of his flute, Miró gathered beasts through his pencils. They gnaw a brick, nibble an almond; bad-tempered, they are always ready for a quarrel, to bite and scratch each other. At times they give their animal squeaks, then, head over heels, on the planks of a lunatic theater made of raisin bread buttered with soap, they put on a show to an audience of ants. Blood pours from a gouged eye and splatters the jellyfish, which slowly flap with the wind currents. These horrible creatures are sometimes haggard, never innocent, certainly perverse and satisfied to be so. They fornicate right on the page, drowning it in their green, red, dingy sperm, tart as lemon, corrosive as sulphuric acid. They occupy the entire surface, well settled in a space where they frisk at their ease. The composition never goes off track. They insist on holding the forestage, take their places within the set perimeter, gesticulate to the point of breathlessness, and then, after skidding, smash up against the foot of a triangle, which, indifferent, decides to sit down and consume, with great slurps of the tongue, an ice cream cone disgorging a colony of beetles.

In these works, Miró compiled a repertory of forms, nocturnal tales, and aerial adventures that would fill the reservoirs of his future imaginings. Unlike Kandinsky, who composed an alphabet of abstract forms, letters, syllables, and words to use in various combinations, Miró garnered and stored up lines, spots, articulations, crisscrosses, angles, targets, and spirals so that, at the right moment and with unfettered hand and restless brain, he could take them up again, manipulate them anew, give them new meanings by changing their colors, distributing them to the four corners of the sheet, turning them upside down, switching right and left, front and behind, foot and sex, stars and butterflies. Eye alert, pencil or brush at the ready, Miró, open to all possibilities, looked to a scorch on his paper, a splatter or blob on the drawing board, a knot in the wood to trigger off the enigmatic release that never failed to make him take up the dance again from association to association. The latent, unformulated desire would then uncoil on the page, there revealing and engraving itself. Mentally stripping himself, Miró laid himself open, accepted the risk of losing himself in order to, at last, find himself. Each picture signed was a leaf fallen from the tree of Miró, planted in the center of the farm at Montroig.

The man was stubborn; *quit* was not in his vocabulary. As early as 1938, he wrote that he would like to try his hand "at sculpture, pottery, prints, to have a press," with the specific aim of going beyond "easel painting, insofar as possible...which in my opinion pursues a petty aim...[in order to] get closer...to the broad mass of human beings who have always been in my thoughts" ("Je rêve d'un grand atelier," *XXe Siècle* 1, no. 2, 1938, in Dupin, p. 432).

The presence in Barcelona of Josep Llorens Artigas, his old friend from difficult times and a ceramicist of great talent who had carried out works for Raoul Dufy and Albert Marquet, gave him his

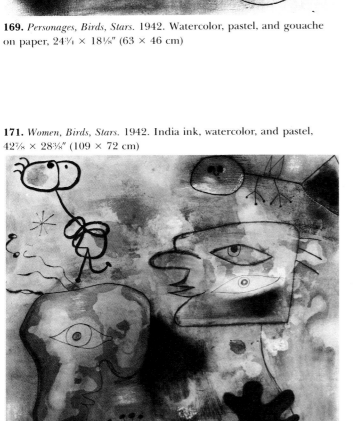

169. *Personages, Birds, Stars.* 1942. Watercolor, pastel, and gouache on paper, 24¾ × 18⅛″ (63 × 46 cm)

170. *Woman in the Night.* 1942. Watercolor and charcoal, 24⅜ × 18⅛″ (62 × 46 cm)

171. *Women, Birds, Stars.* 1942. India ink, watercolor, and pastel, 42⅞ × 28⅜″ (109 × 72 cm)

172. *Woman, Bird, Stars.* 1942. Pen and ink and watercolor, 12¼ × 9½″ (31 × 24 cm)

173. *Personage, Bird, Stars.* 1944. Pen and India ink over watercolor on canvas, 15 × 18⅛″ (38 × 46 cm). Fundació Miró, Barcelona

174. *Woman and Bird in Front of the Sun.* 1944. Oil on canvas, 23⅝ × 29⅛″ (60 × 74 cm)

175. *Women, Bird, Stars.* 1942. Pencil, watercolor, and pastel, 23⅝ × 40½″ (60 × 103 cm)

opportunity. Even if the audacities of his onetime fellow-student made Artigas slightly uneasy, Miró could have confidence in him. Firmly decided to break the rules of pottery, Miró requested, in order to limit the damage, a number of defective pots and forms on which his imagination could do what it wished. As happens with the naive or the poets, to the innocents go the spoils, so the meticulous, careful Miró was amazed at what he came up with. Thanks to the advice of his expert technician friend, the results went beyond his most optimistic hopes. And so, in 1944, there began a regular collaboration rich in unexpected initiatives and exceptional successes.

This was artisans' work, cooperative work in an atmosphere of camaraderie and mutual understanding, from which Miró, saddened by the recent death of his mother, could draw the reassuring warm sentiment of once again being helped, as when he was a small child. In addition, there was the presence of fire, which stirs up in all who draw near it deep primitive and unconscious reveries. Bound up with all the great themes of life, these reveries speak of man's earliest experiences.

Thanks to the potter's fire, Miró finally won the right to his place in the tribal circle alongside the primitive he met in his imagination. Now, perhaps, in the proximity of the glowing kiln with its promise of so many projects to come, lulled by the song of the flames, he could go back to the drawing of a cottage he had made as a small boy and, after so many years, at last draw in a reassuring swirl of smoke from its chimney.

176. *Women, Birds, Stars.* 11 May 1942. Charcoal, pen and India ink, watercolor, and gouache, 35⅜ × 16⅞″ (90 × 43 cm). Fundació Miró, Barcelona

THE WALL DECORATIONS, 1946–1972

"The brilliance of ceramic seduced me: it is like sparks. And then there is the struggle with the elements: earth, fire.... I am very much a fighter. You have to know how to control the fire when you make ceramics." —TO YVON TAILLANDIER

Easel painting sustains a certain constraint: that of solitary confinement. In the best of cases, a canvas is acquired by an art lover for the personal enjoyment of himself and his friends. It does not leave his home again unless by chance loaned to an exhibition. Only works owned by museums are accessible to everyone.

When, like Miró, an artist feels the need for a wider audience, he must seek a way out of the closed circles to which artworks are usually confined. A painter needs to have his work seen. He must have the courage, not always easy, to accept a variety of opinions and frequent misunderstandings. If and when he becomes appreciated, even adulated, he will be able to verify—to his distress—the gap between his intention and the way his work is seen and interpreted. Given the inevitable complexity of human relations, the disturbing delusions of communication between human beings, this is the normal state of affairs. A sensitive, thin-skinned artist may sometimes bridle. Censorious criticisms, whether from experts or ordinary persons, are reprehensible; even if an artist is wrong, he is still striving to share with others what is deepest, weightiest, most fraught with meaning in himself and others. Despite all the mistakes they may make, artists remain the conscience of the world. Civilizations survive through their works, which, viewed as documents, let us reconstitute the history and thinking of the past.

Miró's major retrospective at the Museum of Modern Art, New York, in 1941 and his numerous gallery shows, at Pierre Matisse's in particular, greatly enhanced his reputation in the United States, where he had admiring friends, actively interested museum directors, and enterprising collectors. His work was already influencing American painters of the younger generations. The wartime refugees from France, Max Ernst and André Masson especially, had established close relations with the American artists, which left their mark on both sides.

Western painting may be an international language, but it is shaped by geography. It is rooted in a place, a particular history, a society, a culture; in transplanting it, one always runs a risk. After several years of solitude, Miró felt ready to take that risk. He looked forward to pitting himself against that continent, with its brief but brilliant history, against a forceful society subject to a different psychology, different rules and laws, a different scale. A man of the Mediterranean, Miró needed to experience the unknown winds of the Atlantic and the Pacific in his own sails. Moreover, the fervid libertarian could not help but be drawn to the

country that had supported Europe in its struggle against fascism. In short, everything more or less conspired toward an encounter.

In order to satisfy his desire to address a mass audience, Miró had to move from the intimate handwriting of the watercolors produced in the musical retreat of his studio to the architectural, the monumental. This was a test of strength, a new world to explore. Either he would make a perfect leap across the gap or fall. Such compelling challenges were natural to Miró.

Monumental art is no mere matter of dimensions. It involves being aware of a space and of appropriate proportions. It will not tolerate the nebulous, the approximate, the unconsidered play of the hand. A miniature by Jean Fouquet can be as monumental as a portrait from Fayum or a Romanesque fresco. The secret lies in the union or contrast between solid and empty parts, the equilibrium of forms and their relationship, the effective distribution of colors, the exploitation of a space where each part finds its complete vigor of expression. All this is a natural gift, the fruit of a particular set of mind.

Miró, we know, was a master of the art of placing forms and colors where aesthetically the eye looks for them, and he knew equally well how to short-circuit expectations and surprise us. Even if he had recently devoted several years to gouaches, watercolors, and drawings, his graphic approach and his colors, in their placement and intensity, had all the authority required for work on a larger scale. This was amply proved by the superb series of canvases of 1945 (plates 185–87), which brought him so much renown. For all the power of their strongly marked rhythm, it does not overwhelm the secondary or latent image arising from emphases and details that the eye regroups. Becoming superposed, those two ways of seeing intermingle, foster a poetic ambiguity from which each in turn profits. Miró could pass with remarkable ease from the meditative watercolor to the brilliantly colored canvas with large isolated dancing figures ricocheting off each other in a high-tension space. Thus, everything predestined him for the difficult test of mural decoration.

During those years, Miró had continued to work at ceramics in collaboration with Artigas. He took deep satisfaction from working with the fire. When the glazes are painted on the raw ceramics, they are gray and clayey, taking on color and intensity only with firing. To control the fire calls for measuring, dosing, anticipating, sometimes even using trickery. Before reopening the kiln, it is impossible to know if the piece is a total loss or a complete success, and the tension of discovery is enthralling. Pottery is akin to an alchemist's or a poet's reverie, permitting the unconscious to penetrate to the earth's entrails, to primordial heat, to relive ancient

177. *The Wall of the Moon.* 1957–58. Ceramic, 9′ 10⅛″ × 24′ 7¼″
(3 × 7.5 m). UNESCO Headquarters, Paris

and buried experiences. Holding in one's hands a still-hot plaque and seeing the brilliant colors that have emerged on the terra cotta or stoneware must bring a profound and solemn joy, similar to the feelings evoked by a birth. From the belly of the kiln to the first cry of the colors, to the perfection of the shapes or even their defects, all the symbols are present. For a poet it means living, in the true sense, a revelation.

Miró continued these efforts into 1946. Stubborn, meticulous, and, above all, attentive, he sought to arouse the reactions of glazes on regular or irregular plaques, awaiting patiently or anxiously the fire's verdict. Successes and disappointments were shared with his old friend Artigas. Miró himself has said how much he loves teamwork, where procedures are discussed and cautions and advice dispensed and where bold ventures may be either rewarded or penalized. He learned the old techniques and the methods and secrets gathered from experience or discovered by intuition and shared his own experiences. The potter's workshop is like the laboratory of Doctor Faust and his initiates, where master and assistant together penetrate the occult and sometimes unpredictable laws of both chemistry and life.

The Ceramic Walls at UNESCO Headquarters in Paris

In 1955, when the director and architects of the new UNESCO headquarters in Paris proposed that Miró decorate two freestanding outdoor walls, he naturally thought of adorning them in ceramics. The two walls, set at a right angle, were to be 9′10″ (3 meters) high

and, respectively, 49′2″ (15 meters) and 24′7″ (7.5 meters) long. He could count on an adequate team of helpers and whatever materials he would need, as well as the assistance of his friend and colleague Artigas. After acquainting himself with the site and the building under construction, he slowly worked out his idea. Contrasting the highly glazed ceramic tiles with the raw reinforced concrete of the building itself, he set the sun on the large wall, *The Wall of the Sun*, the moon on the small one, *The Wall of the Moon* (plate 177), a large red disk corresponding with a blue crescent. With the overall setting in mind, he opted for very strong colors and, as he subsequently explained, "brutal and dynamic" black graphisms contrasting with forms "calm, colored in flat tints or checkerboards."

Very conscious of their responsibilities, Miró and Artigas, before settling on the plan, made a pilgrimage to the sources. They went to Santillana del Mar to see the Romanesque Church of Collegiata, to the caves of Altamira for the prehistoric wall paintings, to the Catalan Museum of Art in Barcelona for its early frescoes, and finally to Gaudí's Parque Güell, where that strange genius had utilized odds and ends of ceramics for decorations of astounding imaginativeness. Two discoveries remained engraved on their memories: the walls of the Collegiata "eaten by damp" and the immense disk "laying bare the rock" on one of the sustaining walls of Gaudí's park.

With Miró's approval, Artigas proposed a mixed procedure: "Fireclay covered by white slip, the whole fired at 1,000 degrees Centigrade and then glazed with a stoneware enamel ground, different for each square, fired at 1,300 degrees. Then the firing for the decoration, glazing and color, at 1,000 degrees. It was all baked with wood, which permits effects unobtainable with gas, coal,

Mural Painting for the Hilton Terrace Plaza Hotel

or electricity." The first two hundred and fifty regular-shaped plaques fired in thirty-three batches proved unsatisfactory and were destroyed: four thousand kilograms of clay, two hundred and fifty of glazes, and ten tons of wood went by the boards.

After this painful setback, the project was reconsidered, the ground material rethought, and the decision made to utilize plaques of different sizes, as in the magnificent stone structures of Romanesque edifices. After that, Miró wrote,

... it was up to me to step in and transfer my design and paint with colored glazes the elements laid out on the ground. There, once again, my forms were modified. As for the colors, I had to rely on Artigas's knowledge because, before firing, glazes do not yet have their color. But, despite the precautions that can be taken, in the last resort the master of the works is the fire: its action is unpredictable and its penalty heavy. It is that which, to my eyes, makes this means of expression worthwhile. Further difficulty: the large dimensions of the surface I had to paint. Certain forms, certain lines had to be laid down in a single movement in order to preserve their dynamism and original effect. For this I made use of a palm-fiber broom. Artigas gasped when he saw me grab the broom to lay down forms measuring from five to six meters, running the risk of compromising therewith the work of many months (Miró, "Ma dernière oeuvre est un mur," *Derrière le Miroir*, nos. 107–9, 1958, pp. 24–29).

This decoration in sumptuous material—in the best sense of the word—was greeted with admiration by the public and critics alike and was honored in 1958 by the Guggenheim International Award of the Guggenheim Foundation.

With the 1947 commission for a vast mural decoration for the Gourmet Restaurant at the Hilton Terrace Plaza Hotel on the top story of a Cincinnati skyscraper (plate 178), Miró's reputation in the United States was confirmed. On a surface three meters high and ten meters long (9' 10" by 32' 9¾"), he realized an astonishing frieze in which forms circulated along the wall like figures on a carrousel. The eye no sooner turns from one form standing out against the blue ground than it is seized by another, and then by the next, a highly amusing cavalcade of little men dropped from the moon, strange and motley personages, hook-beaked creatures, variegated feathered serpents from across the Mexican border. If the contortions of its various elements and their calculated disproportions to each other call to mind the enervated, sometimes cruel action of Mayan or Incan stone reliefs, on the other hand, the forcefulness of the flat shapes, the graphic elegance, the cadenced rhythm, and the surprise of the unexpected give this circular frieze a cheerful briskness that tones down the bizarreness of its content.

Obedient to a regular rhythm, large vertical forms settle in the space like pillars. They are surrounded by small forms—marionettes, hooks, mustaches, bull's-eyes, triangles, points, circles—overlapping or juxtaposed, which pretend to be stable while on the edge of a movement that remains, however, implicit. It calls to mind the runner who straightens up and stretches in the instant preceding the spring of his takeoff. Miró's drollery does not generally come from the extravagance of his personages and the disconcerting associations they spark off but, most often, from the particular placement of his forms in space and their brilliant coloring. The exhilaration they arouse in us is akin to the marvel we feel when a trapeze artist succeeds in a perilous leap.

178. *Mural Painting.* 1947. Oil on canvas, 9′10″ × 32′9¾″ (3 × 10 m). Gourmet Restaurant, Hilton Terrace Plaza Hotel, Cincinnati

179. *Mural Painting.* 1950–51. Oil on canvas, 6′2″ × 19′5½″ (1.88 × 5.93 m). Fogg Art Museum, Cambridge, Mass. Originally for the Graduate Center, Harvard University

180. *Mural Painting.* 1953. Oil on canvas, 6′4¾″ × 12′4⅞″ (1.95 × 3.78 m). Solomon R. Guggenheim Museum, New York

Mural Painting for the Graduate Center, Harvard University

In 1951, the Harvard Graduate School commissioned Miró for a mural for its dining hall (plate 179). For this wall painting of 1.88 by 5.93 meters (6′2″ by 19′5½″), he chose a different approach. Very large forms with three main emphases—the two compact areas of the outer ends and the lighter and more varied center, accompanied by a very strong graphism—appear to take possession of the space, adhering firmly to the ground, which is lightly modulated in gray, blue, green, and ocher. Patches of color, in flat areas or broken up by checkerboard patterns, set up contrasts between light and dark and fight each other for dominance. Bewildered little men, a rocky pumpkin-head, and a portico-personage (which would reappear in both ceramics and sculpture) are juxtaposed against the ground. Uncharacteristically, they are calm and ironical, and the empty spaces around them have a fine transparency and harmonious design.

Everything holds together and follows along cohesively, making this a classical composition insofar as the elements remain well-contained within the format of the support. The eye stops where the canvas folds over the stretcher. This is a traditional constructional principle to which Miró remained curiously faithful throughout his life. In general, his well-knit compositions are centered, then elaborated to the edges of the canvas. This principle, which Monet in the wake of the Romantics infringed in his desire for fluidity, was taken up again in Europe, in a new spirit, by the young painters of the Abstraction Lyrique tendency, as it would soon be named. Like the camera's eye, theirs is in motion, appearing to shift and glide across the landscape or the composition. The forms thus appear like particular instants in a long motion-picture dolly shot and give the impression of continuing beyond the limits of the picture. To stability these artists preferred energy.

Ceramic Wall Decoration for the Graduate Center, Harvard University

When the large mural painting for Harvard was removed to the Fogg Art Museum, Miró was asked to replace it with a ceramic. With his ever-active inventiveness, Miró rejected the idea of a copy in another material, choosing instead to embrace a new experience and a new risk (plate 181). Moreover, in the intervening ten years, his style had changed considerably, and he felt ready to apply to ceramics his current preoccupations in painting. He had attained a degree of freedom of movement that he was resolved to hold on to and which offered little leeway for either the precautions or the technical uncertainties he had encountered not so long ago with the UNESCO walls. This reflected not impatience or nervousness but a new way of experiencing the act of painting itself, which was contrary to precautions, calculations, and procrastination, instead going directly to the heart of the composition.

Thus, Miró decided now to work directly on the 128 regular-sized plaques of fireclay laid out on the ground and already covered with the unfired inert glazes of the background. "Using a pointed wooden stick which only with difficulty abraded the stratum of enamel glaze," he managed to trace very quickly a clumsy sketch. Next, armed with a brush and a black stoneware glaze, he worked into the rhythm of his body movement to find the right amplitude of gesture as he drew on the surface a series of interweaving traceries from which emerged personages born from the interlacing of the lines and the irregularity of the flat patches. Then, with considerable impetuosity, he flung down a spray of more or less dense droplets of different sizes as a way of linking the background as he imagined it with the highly diversified broad black lines he had laid out no less impetuously. Finally, to find the right position and rhythm for the few patches of blue, green, red, and yellow he wanted, he laid down shapes cut out of paper. "Little by little, he found the exact place and size for each accent of color and their

181. *Ceramic Mural.* Executed by Josep Llorens Artigas. 1960. Ceramic, 6' 6¾" × 19' 8¼" (2 × 6 m). Graduate Center, Harvard University, Cambridge, Mass.

articulation with the rhythm of the whole.... A chrome red, a cobalt blue, a uranium yellow, and a copper green fired at only 900 degrees gave those patches the desired intensity" (Joan Gardy Artigas, "La Céramique pour Harvard," *Derrière le Miroir*, no. 123, February 1961).

This new strategy in the ceramic medium was proof of Miró's mastery. His freedom of composition is also the sign of a great penetration and a strong inner assurance. More, this brilliant work with its strong and surging rhythm shows itself the product of a man who gave himself entirely and, in all his various forms of expression, attained unity.

After the Dutch group De Stijl (1917–32) had championed an architecture stripped of unfunctional ornamentation, devoid of the curve, and enlivened only by color, an interest in integrating the arts returned only gradually to the programs of young architects. Among the artists, however, only a rare few were interested by such projects, which called for them to work in a team and come to terms with the requirements of construction. The architects clashed with individualistic-minded artists, and the artists felt themselves poorly used by those in charge of construction, the latter generally being somewhat deficient in artistic culture, which, particularly in France, had been neglected for decades in the curriculum of the higher professional schools. Miró's ceramic murals, superbly decorative and perfectly adapted to their role, are an example for all who believe there can be a dialogue between the man in the street and the contemporary artist. Through his successes, Miró encouraged further collaboration such as existed already on other levels.

Mural Painting for the Solomon R. Guggenheim Museum

In 1953, the Solomon R. Guggenheim Museum of New York commissioned from Miró a huge canvas, measuring almost two by four meters (roughly six by twelve feet), dimensions classing it among wall paintings (plate 180). At this time, Miró was aiming at a particularly frank and powerful painting, and in this new monumental undertaking his body, muscles, and gestures could enter into play with all the expansiveness called for by that new approach. It was an ideal occasion to go beyond easel painting, which he had found constricting. He sought to wed spontaneity with an appropriate expenditure of energy in order to communicate its full ardor.

Painters on both sides of the Atlantic at that time were feeling a new need for a close link between the material itself and their own physical movements. They hoped to devise a personal or, more ambitiously, entirely new conception of space, structured on the rhythm and sweep of the artist's gestures and bringing him into active physical union with his painting. Jackson Pollock had already embarked on this hazardous venture a few years earlier in the United States. The aggressiveness of the gesture can be read directly on the canvas. Such gestures in front of a stretch of white canvas represent also a new way of crystallizing time, whose representation has, by the nature of the art, always obsessed and eluded painters.

The approach Miró chose, although related, was less radical. His picture ground was boldly swept, rubbed, brushed, irregularly leaving traces of the vehemently or impetuously wielded instrument. Such rapid, even instantaneous work confronted and reacted with the slow and caressing work. (Note that almost all the

terms we are using to try to convey the visual impression of Miró's canvas are borrowed from the vocabulary of time and movement.)

On this richly nuanced, active ground, prepared at length and much heightened in effect, Miró laid down a strong red and blue center and then inscribed broad, barbarous black signs, accented here and there by green or red lozenges. A vivid yellow and an energetic green resonate like the blow of a fist on a table to either side of the central divinity: an altar raised to the new god Robot. His rectangular head bows the long stem of his neck into a curve, his green and red metallic face resembles the radiator of an American automobile or a menacing vacuum cleaner, ready to swallow his own bloodstained ceremonial robe.

This was probably not the interpretation that Miró gave the work at the time, although he might not have refused it. He was preoccupied with questions of painting: how could he make the dreamed and ardently sought image coincide with what, in the fever of work, took shape before his eyes? For all his willfully independent spirit, how could he escape the reflexes imposed by a type of culture? America and Europe, active in unequal measure, were at conflict within him.

182. *Ceramic Mural.* 1968. Ceramic, 6′ 4¾″ × 40′ 2¼″ (2 × 12.25 m). Fondation Maeght, Saint-Paul-de-Vence, France

Other Wall Decorations

Between 1964 and 1972, in Sankt Gallen, Saint-Paul-de-Vence (plate 182), New York, Osaka, Barcelona, Paris, and Zurich, Miró was busy adorning walls and gardens with red, green, yellow, and blue plaques, flinging buckets of enamel, covering huge surfaces with splashes, making all these gravitate around a solar mechanism, new galaxies, and planets in a sky unknown to everyone but himself. With such audaciously formulated interrogations he hoped to shake up people's ingrained ways of thinking.

If his poetic forms are charged with profound symbolic significance, so must his acts and gestures. In 1968, he committed to the water a *Goddess of the Sea* in a grotto the size of a cathedral looking out at Juan Gulf, not far from the Fondation Maeght.

1944–1950

183. *Painting*

184. *Woman and Bird in the Night.* November 1945. Gouache on cork, 4⅜ × 39⅜″ (11 × 100 cm)

"I work a long time, sometimes years, on a single picture. But during all that time, there are moments, sometimes very long ones, during which I do not concern myself with it."

"The fact that a canvas may remain for years under way in my atelier doesn't worry me. On the contrary, when I am rich in canvases that have a beginning lively enough to trigger off a series of rhymes, a new life, new living things, I am happy."
—TO YVON TAILLANDIER

The line and the spot of color are for Miró two means perpetually placed in parallel. They either begin a dialogue or resist each other, or then again Miró will stake all on one and take away from color what he has just granted to line, or the reverse. Thus colors and graphisms unite, play together with equal forces in a dosage of great subtlety. All experiments are possible, all possibilities solicited. Setting aside the scientific coldness implied by the word *experiment* and giving it instead its full measure of human density, one finds that for Miró it meant freedom of mind, physical involvement in everything undertaken, and a profound commitment associated with the most attractive aspect of play, of the game itself.

The original meaning of *game*—struggle—has become blurred, and the word itself devalued. But games and play, with their fixed rules, brought human beings stage by stage from savagery to culture. Since to play a game is to accept rules and constraints, it automatically arouses the most personal and spontaneous reactions. In chemical terms, audacity, or risk-taking, is the precipitate. The game rewards spirit and invention with resolution of the problem or victory. And, since in its origins a game was a battle against death, this gives it a sacred character. It is the test, the obstacle that calls on all a person's forces to remove it so as to discover himself, in both senses of the word: to move from cover to the open, thus putting himself in danger, and to look at that which is hidden or supposed to remain hidden. Revelation is behind the rules, and there is no doubt that that is what Miró sought from canvas to canvas.

Every picture Miró produced between 1944 and 1950 turned out

to be an extraordinary fugue of color and bouncy line. Color and line balance each other, challenge one another. Besides canvas in traditional formats, Miró also used coarsely woven pieces of cloth or sacking whose frayed ends were left as they were. In 1944 especially, he did not hesitate to use India ink, charcoal, pastels, and watercolors on canvas, since new chemical advances had made it possible to fix them. Drawing lightly and airily with a delicate, alert, inventive line, he exploited the moistness of his paint ground to make his color or line blur, so that the line thickened and took on unpredictable arborescences, and a drop of India ink became surrounded with proliferations like colonies of mosses spreading over a tree trunk.

In this period, Miró demonstrated a predilection for broken lines and zigzags, and he flung handfuls of stars across his surfaces. More than ever, he cultivated disproportion—large authoritarian personages with wooden-shoe heads, mounted on plant stems, encounter very small wide-eyed creatures with the sulky look of the perennially harried: infantile beings lorded over by giant parents. His spun-wire line is so supple it coils back on itself, joyous or droll like Calder's when he whipped life into the hesitant acrobats and animal trapeze-artists of his circus (1926–28).

The carefully worked paint grounds, often enigmatic, tended to keep to a light register: whitish gray, modulated gray, lyrical blue, greens, various earth colors. Now, however, they were treated not with the prodigious delicacy of earlier periods but laid on in chalky or silky manner. Relatively inconspicuous, they seem just the right supports for such explosions of color spots, such elongations or tangles of lines, to which they remain subordinate. The forms are so arranged that they almost always look as if they are about to jump on one foot and play hopscotch. They leap over one another. Although all are well in place, they seem guided by a desire to go someplace else. Nonchalantly, they exploit a fixity that does not in fact exist. Rarely do they touch ground; the lower border of the canvas is not the earth we unconsciously take it to be but, instead, the illusory limit of an aerial space. The pumpkins with swollen

185. *Woman in the Night.* 18 April 1945. Oil on canvas, 51⅛ × 76¾″ (130 × 195 cm). Private collection, New York

bellies are balloons, afloat. "Aerial freedom speaks, illumines, flies" (G. Bachelard, *L'Air et les songes*, Paris, 1948, p. 74). Our unconscious takes pleasure in such weightless forms, free as air. In our dreams, flying is a pleasure seeking satisfaction, and this is one of the secret reasons for the sheer joy we feel looking at Miró's works: they lead to the dance, as Léonide Massine said in connection with his ballet *Jeux d'enfants*.

The large canvases of 1945 (plates 185–87), among Miró's best known, largely set a definitive style. They boast amplitude—almost all are large—simplicity, invention, a felicitous airiness, an accomplished easiness. But the simplicity is only apparent; with Miró, everything is complex. Together or separately, they have a lively, eye-catching rhythm. Patches of color perfectly distributed on the surface strike the flowing line like billiard balls, each time hitting their target. Then, within the transparent forms, an organized circuit of relay stations, stops, and crossings end up establishing a traffic system, an insidious geometry where the eye is caught and held, like a lark in a net. The eye becomes exasperated by so many accidents and surprises that make it leap. It ricochets, evoking the same wonder aroused by a swiftly flung stone skipping several times across the calm surface of a pool. In this way, the instant, the wish, and the surprise are brought into perfect harmony almost unconsciously. An interesting note: all these canvases are on light-colored grounds except two, both of which have titles referring to music.

The Bullfight

The Bullfight (plate 186), which Miró donated in 1947 to the Musée National d'Art Moderne in Paris, is not preoccupied with subtleties of time. As befits its theme, it registers a moment of time arrested. The gray ground, worked in irregular checkerboard shapes, appears silvered due to an undercoat of sienna abundantly mixed

with white. It gives an overall effect of Oriental shot silk. A continuous outline, without solid patches or taperings, delineates a bull. Placed parallel to and facing an imaginary public that includes the viewer, the bull confronts us, more terrified than terrifying, despite a mouth armed with sharp and shining teeth. Two round eyes, one black, red, and green, the other blue, red, and black, are joined by a third eye in red, black, and white, which floats over the beast's head and lends it a mythological or sacred air. On the left, a corkscrew personage is tangled up in the folds of a cape, while at the upper right a ridiculous matador is incorporated into a large black oval traversed by the yellow lightning of the mortal *estocada*. This canvas demonstrates Miró's dislike for the perilous exercise of Cretan origin enthusiastically embraced by Spaniards. That macabre and bloody pavane was foreign to Miró, who remained loyal instead to the *sardana*, the Catalan national dance that had been described by Homer. Death, considered by Surrealist painters and poets as the definitive castration and which, on those grounds, obsessed them, was treated by another artist of their group with a confusion of fine fabrics and watered silks, torn corals, pulleys, sewing machines, pianos, and masks surging from the shadows. Miró's picture, on the other hand, relies on no more than the power of painting to suggest its protest, making it an excellent example of what set its author apart from the students of dream painting.

Woman Listening to Music

This work, dated 11 May 1945 (plate 187), is particularly inventive and fertile. Five light cell-shapes in different sizes make holes in the black ground. They contain what at first look like different signs; on closer view, they appear to be stages in the metamorphosis of a globe mounted on two verticals crossed by a horizontal. The basic sign is kneaded, transformed, turned upside down, its arms ripped out of joint, its body twisted on itself, a

139

186. *The Bullfight.* 8 October 1945. Oil on canvas, 44⅞ × 57½″ (114 × 146 cm). Musée National d'Art Moderne, Centre Georges Pompidou, Paris

187. *Woman Listening to Music.* 11 May 1945.
Oil on canvas, 51⅛ × 63¾" (130 × 162 cm).
Private collection, United States

coiled arabesque; our mind easily transforms the white or black woman into an eighth or thirty-second note. All around, touches of color punctuate or prick the opaque surface. They are precise, dry, isolated, but here and there a wavy line links a sphere and a point that resonates with color. Above all this, a toothy profile with wide-awake bull's-eye seems alert to what is about to happen.

This picture poses a possible poetic equivalence to music. Its coloring might call to mind the music of Igor Stravinsky, its subtlety, punctuation, and acrid refinement that of Arnold Schönberg. The color strikes the surface, dilating or contracting the space, producing bow strokes, hammering percussions, tingling triangles; the note, as noted in the cells ringing its changes, unrolls, stretches out, holds onto the circle, where suddenly it emerges and inscribes itself.

But here again, exploiting as if by chance a procedure already tested by primitive painters, Miró makes use of simultaneity. Thus, in our imagination each circle may contain an isolated moment of a continuous movement. Time in its flow, the chief characteristic of music, is laid out here on the surface of a painting. Times juxtaposed recompose a duration. At the same time, Miró has situated this work very close to the procedures of poetry, another art of time, which by the opposition of words contrives to create intervals, by subtle typographical dispositions to telescope time, to hold it back, and even, within the framework of a white page, to abolish it or, perhaps, make it explode. This difficult undertaking is apparently more delicate in poetry than in painting, because the poet is less well equipped, having fewer means. The poet is more harrassed by his syntax, the painter less tied down to his. Such relationships between word, space, time, and color in painting and poetry are very ancient and recur repeatedly. They were expressed anew in Apollinaire's *calligrammes* but go back to antiquity; examples of such picture-poems from the third century B.C. as well as from the fourteenth and eighteenth centuries, among others, have been anthologized (in "Les Ancêtres des idéogrammes," *L'Esprit nouveau*, no. 27, 1925).

The Red Sun Gnaws at the Spider, The Diamond Smiles at the Twilight

All the works from 1948–50 are marked by a strong tension and a great activity rich in daring sorties, to borrow a military term. The canvases are profuse in signs, graphisms, writings. Spontaneity and sudden decisions combine with precise determination and attentive care. In *The Diamond Smiles at the Twilight* (plate 189), the nervous line snakes across the canvas; three vaporous black, red, and yellow stellar bodies are held in place against a Veronese green ground by a network of black lines, which become tangled and change thickness in their course. In turn fluid or jagged, in long flourishes, the line relaxes, stretches, swerves suddenly—and the diamond smiles at the twilight.

For a long time, Miró made no distinction between signs and personages. The frontier between their identities is often tenuous. He felt no need to submit to categories, as he was disinclined to define sectors. For him, everything was in movement. Things imperceptibly slide from one to the other. Nature itself, after all, is ambiguous. Male is also female, and the feminine embraces also a masculine principle. Only chemistry involves simple bodies; with the human being, everything is complex.

From canvas to canvas, Miró revealed his need to allow the signs

188. *The Red Sun Gnaws at the Spider.* 1948. Oil on canvas, 29⅞ × 37¾″ (76 × 96 cm). Private collection, Belgium

142

189. *The Diamond Smiles at the Twilight.* 24 January 1948. Oil on canvas, 38⅛ × 51⅛" (97 × 130 cm). Fundació Miró, Barcelona

their autonomy. If at first they mingled with his personages, now they made their entrances surreptitiously. Even upside down they have the power to schematize a human form, and they sometimes seem to derive from an ancient barbarian alphabet: with their red spots, heavy black bars, and broad brushstrokes, they seem to have been born fully armed. *The Red Sun Gnaws at the Spider* (plate 188) is a skillful combination of human and archaic suggestions. The breadth of the tracks left by the brush implies full involvement of the painter's own body, which give them the authority of a gesture of command. It makes an interesting foil to *At the Bottom of the Shell* (plate 196) and *The Moon* (plate 197), whose signs and personages seem to be born out of one another. Hybrid beings, invented forms, disconcerting or bantering graffiti, they have the unsettling power of naive or primitive representations.

Woman in Front of the Sun, Canvas-Object

On a blue ground strewn with stars, captive of the red sun, her face gnawed by an enormous green, yellow, and white eye with a black pupil, the *Woman in Front of the Sun* (plate 194) is a poor little cat deified one day by Ramses III in a fit of melancholy and commemorated on a frieze of his solar temple at Medinet Habu. *Canvas-Object* of 1949 (plate 195), combining painted sign,

sewing, and relief, seems like some long-buried debris unearthed by the pickax of an Eygptian peasant staggered by his find. But the game is more complex than that, because this small canvas is indebted to no known ancient civilization and yet brings one to mind—the power of suggestion of the metaphor.

Painting (Personages and Dog in Front of the Sun)

For this painting (plate 198), one may imagine a moral tale for all those who do not believe in the salubrious virtues of humor. This, then, is a family scene. A gentleman with an astonished air seems to wear a pince-nez. His feet, turned outward, drag along the ground—a Sunday stroll, to judge by the hat the lady wears. A little boy, still "wrapped up" in his mother, is so small his head seems at ground level. He must be the gentleman's son, for the good reason that he too wears a pince-nez. The tangled lines suggest that he has a problem with a little dog, or perhaps a butterfly. All of them seem to be dressed in their Sunday best: father in a black topcoat, mama wearing a dress with large blue, black, and green squares, child in, appropriately, small red and blue checks. If children care more for balloons than for the sun, he need not worry: the sun will be a red balloon if one reads its position toward the bottom of the composition. Why a star?

190. *Women and Birds at Sunrise.* 14 February 1946. Oil on canvas, 21¼ × 25⅝" (54 × 65 cm). Fundació Miró, Barcelona

191. *Women in the Night.* 11 June 1946. Oil, gouache, watercolor, and pastel on canvas, 13 × 25¼″ (33 × 64 cm). Private collection, United States

192. *The Bird-Arrow.* 17 March 1948. Oil on canvas, 12⅝ × 27⅝″ (32 × 70 cm)

193. *Women, Moon, Star.* 1949. Oil on canvas, 28¾ × 36¼" (73 × 92 cm)

194. *Woman in Front of the Sun.* 1950. Oil on canvas, 25⅝ × 19⅝″ (65 × 50 cm)

195. *Canvas-Object.* 1949. Oil and iron wire on canvas, 8⅝ × 6¼″ (22 × 16 cm)

196. *At the Bottom of the Shell.* 28 March 1948. Oil on canvas, 29⅞ × 37¾″ (76 × 96 cm). Private collection

197. *The Moon.* 23 March 1948. Oil on canvas, 27⅝ × 35⅞″ (70 × 91 cm). Private collection, United States

Because Miró loved them; he attached them where he could, simply for pleasure. A bird making its toilette could just as well have made its nest in the lady's blue, red, and black hat.

Yet, taking everything into account, one could still say: here is a vertical, there a horizontal, and both would like to sit on a circle. Obviously, the experiment failed. The circle slipped off to the right. Furious, exasperated, the lines thereupon transformed themselves into curves, a serious, even indecent failing in straight lines. It all looks unstable. However, nothing is falling, the two situations support each other through their opposition. Out of that contradiction arises a discord that cannot be resolved, especially since Miró, always a connoisseur of ambiguity, decided at the last minute to invert his composition. The top is at the bottom: decidedly, everything is askew in this world, which walks on its head.

This little bourgeois domestic story was probably not in Miró's thoughts when he painted the canvas. However, without too much strain it can be deduced from the forms, colors, and composition. Miró posed himself entirely different problems, whereas his hand, often insubordinate, and his mind, often rebellious, watched for the path to which his underlying desire would lead his decision. So it is that the paint ground is a visual novel in itself. Essence of turpentine, probably from the bowl in which the painter soaked his brushes, was laid on lightly across a rectangle of thick, rough canvas, like an old linen sheet, and left to spread wherever the weave would take it. This made it take on seemingly constructed shapes: net meshes, geometrical cells, flowing streaks, ruches. Every accident gave it a new twist. Almost weightless, it did not sink in but only grazed the surface. The ground breathes so comfortably that the colors had to let it come through; the play between the opaque and the transparent is still one of the pleasures of painting. Perhaps it was to preserve this very intriguing and, to the painter, pleasing ground that one day, when the mood caught him and memories once stored and lost came back, he produced this picture titled *Painting (Inverted Personages)* (Dupin, no. 728) and also *Personages and Dog in Front of the Sun.*

Portrait of a Young Man

Those things labeled *kitsch* manifest such an unfelicitous display of imagination that one is torn between amazement and hilarity. It is an aesthetic form elaborated with undue care to the point of perversion. The Surrealists delightedly and shamelessly practiced it as an outright provocation.

Miró received as a gift, from a second-hand shop, a portrait of a young man born 18 December 1881, who died 4 October 1903. Its beribboned frame was embellished with the ivy of eternal memory and other mortuary flowering plants. Miró could not resist "improving" it and, by that irreverent act, rescued from the oblivion that would otherwise doubtless have been his lot this stout young man with a virile and self-satisfied air, posing for posterity with fist on thigh and seated between two protecting and edifying holy images that can no longer extend any aid to him. Miró's drawn and painted commentary (plate 199), in flagrant contradiction to the naturalistic likeness, lets it be understood that the deceased, who placed himself so advantageously for eternal bliss, may not in fact have been as well-behaved as his mother liked to think. He doubtless enjoyed the good things of life and had various dealings, probably secret, with temptresses; those three curving hairs are Miró's frequent attribute of femaleness. Of course, the sign is left ambiguous, and its primary loyalty is to artistic necessity.

Even if it was not Miró's intention, his unforeseen contribution conferred on this person a longevity he could not have hoped for, and provided him a serious, comfortable, and coveted place, doubtless preferable to the one he himself has inhabited since 1903, in the collection of the Museum of Modern Art, New York.

After eight months in the United States, Miró returned to France in 1948. He received a solo exhibition at the Galerie Maeght, which had already featured his works in the international Surrealist exhibition in 1947, and his paintings, ceramics, and sculpture would continue to be shown in that gallery in the years to come.

149

198. *Painting (Personages and Dog in Front of the Sun).* 9 May 1949. Oil on canvas,
31⅞ × 21⅝″ (81 × 55 cm). Kunstmuseum, Basel. Emmanuel Hoffmann Foundation

199. *Portrait of a Man in a Late Nineteenth Century Frame.* 1950.
Oil on canvas with ornamented wood frame, 57½ × 49¼"
(146 × 125 cm). The Museum of Modern Art, New York

200. *Woman Powdering Herself.* 1949. Oil, watercolor, gouache, and pastel on canvas, 13¾ × 18⅛″ (35 × 46 cm)

201. *Composition with Strings.* 1950. Oil, casein, and string on canvas, 38⅛ × 30¼″ (97 × 77 cm). Stedelijk Museum, Eindhoven

1950-1960

"The picture must be fruitful. It must make a world come to life. Whether one sees there flowers, personages, horses, it doesn't matter, so long as it reveals a world, something living."—TO YVON TAILLANDIER

For Miró, this decade was to be upset by various tribulations. The peace of mind and the concentration governing the rhythm of his work would be put to a hard test. Nonetheless, he moved to a new address in Barcelona with no grave upset in 1950, and it was during that otherwise agitated but creative year that he turned out the large wall painting for Harvard (plate 179).

Never at peace with himself, his imagination always working, Miró now threw himself into producing a series of forceful paintings. Bursting with energy, the sign in these is often associated with very fluid paint or, on the contrary, with a heavy buildup and excess of material. Then again, following the changing inflections of his hand and in the fervor of the instant, he might let a highly charged line run on its own in opposition to precise forms of splendidly glowing color. His paint grounds are irregularly agitated, resembling a sea of clouds and, like them, in flux. They were laid on with brushes by preference old and used, whose uneven bristles left on the canvas bustling colors, splashes, unexpected discharges of paint. In a way, these turbulent grounds speak to us, distress our eyes, which, however, can never stop scrutinizing them, exploring

them. In the very instant the grounds seem about to give up their secret, they conceal it again. At the same time, the dynamism that animates them—a dynamism arising from the fact that each gesture leaves the mark of the act that produced it—is what permits the forms flung on them to live. They seem to hang in the air, to run wild, to hop, to roll around blindly. Graffiti, signs, vivid colors all have their own function, an individual manner almost always strong, even aggressive, and they boldly take possession of the space Miró assigns them.

Henri Focillon, author of the celebrated *La Vie des formes*, distinguished between the "space of life" and the "space of art," in which latter he discerned a "plastic and changing material." The forms "engendered by the motions of an imaginary space...would be...absurd in the ordinary regions of life." For him, this was "a space constructed or destroyed by form, animated by it, molded by it" (*The Life of Forms in Art*, trans. Charles Beecher Hogan and George Kubler, New Haven: Yale University Press, 1942, pp. 19, 21). With Miró, this process seems to be inverted. Space is primary, the form emerges from it. The eye does not fail to register, from time to time, a tension, perhaps even rivalry between them. Focillon's perceptive reflection is more likely to refer to the painting we now think of as classical. But Miró had long before broken with that style. What distinguishes great artists and consummate

202. *Women, Moon, Birds.* 3 November 1950. Oil on canvas, 44⅞ × 57½" (114 × 146 cm). Private collection, Brussels

technicians is their ability to imagine different or entirely new propositions, whose vitality they then demonstrate in their own work.

In his manual activity as painter, in his craft, Miró demonstrated a profound independence. All orthodoxy struck him as suspect. He always liked to paint on the most unpromising materials, was always ready to annex for painting and for art in general materials most people thought bizarre but which he proved were in no way alien to him. Freely, without any qualms, he utilized instruments that, loaded with paint or ink, left on the canvas the most diverse evidence of their passage. Rather than the small, fine or wide, flexible hog or sable brushes most artists use, he preferred old, poorly cleaned brushes, either stiff or rough. The means or procedure in itself mattered little; what counted was the shock produced, the expressive character engendered. To lay down his paint on the surface and build it into impasto, like any careful artisan, he had had to create for himself a repertory of gestures, rhythms, attacks, and the sort of rebounds and releases pianists use. These were his means of obtaining the rugged, velvety, dry, or light effects he desired and might include, for instance, a smoothly begun stroke and a clean cutoff. In certain cases, a broom could serve as well as a brush.

Often his pictures can be read entirely in terms of technique and

craftsmanship, with the eye traveling from surprise to surprise. Spurted or muddy lines, delicate, watery effects, tiny dots or blobs like pastry decorations, and all his other devices open the way, from association to association, to a world rich in perceptions. Miró often further enriched their refinement by giving the devices a rapid inflection or alternating their effects: a bite follows a caress, a fist in the face an exquisite touch. He felt that each such accent or gesture should be clearly readable, even if not always exactly communicable, and should initiate that dialogue between coruscating space and his always expressive form, which seems the common denominator in all these plastic and pictorial essays.

Paintings with Dotting

Late in 1953, Miró systematically cultivated dotting, applying his paint either with the end of a stick or, more probably, a finger, and all the works of the following year show this trait (plates 212, 213, 215). Generally, the stippled dots contrast with the tonality of the form they surround, or they alternate light and dark. They aggregate from place to place, are regular or irregular, disappear at the shift of a curve, skip over a vertical line and reappear along a circle or crescent. These tiny dots, despite their air of innocence,

203. *The Bird Flies Off to the Zone Where Plumage Grows on the Gold-Ringed Hills.*
1950. Oil on canvas, 29⅞ × 37⅜″ (76 × 95 cm)

204. *Dragonfly with Red-Tipped Wings in Pursuit of a Serpent Spiraling Toward a Comet.*
1951. Oil on canvas, 31⅞ × 39⅜″ (81 × 100 cm). Fundació Miró, Barcelona

205. *The Twists of Mustaches Facing the Dazzling Birds.* 1952.
Oil on canvas, 6¼ × 8⅝″ (16 × 22 cm)

206. *Bird.* 1 June 1960. Oil on tar-lined paper

evoke a sense of uncertainty, disquiet. Miró most likely intended them to hold down and fix a line, to imprison a sign, and, above all, to situate both with respect to the picture ground. These girandoles of tiny flashing lights probably signal some doubt about line or sign.

To prevent the sign from escaping, Miró pinioned it in place with these studlike dots; to stop the line from wandering, he gave it a stippled border. The final result is that an indecisive space comes into balance or settles into place.

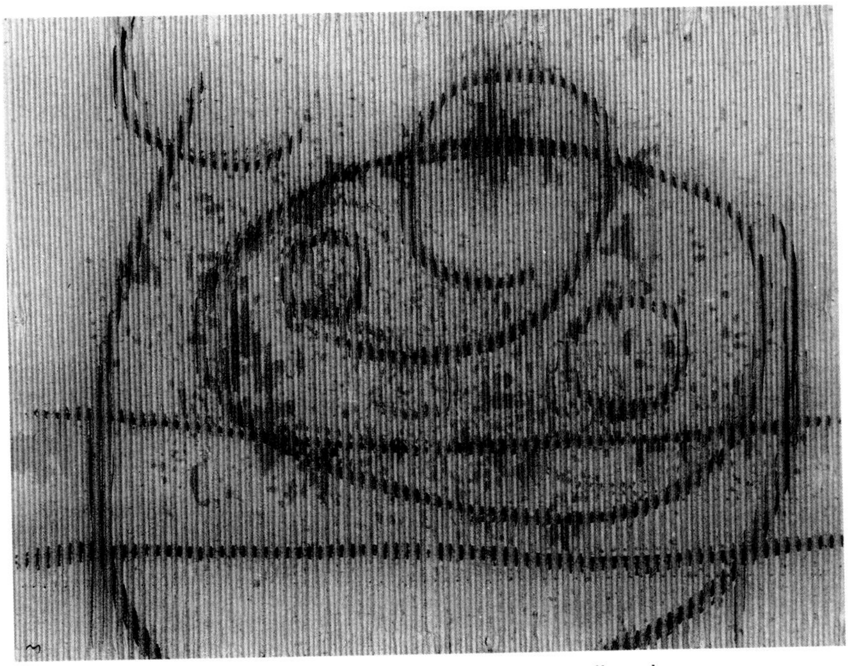

207. *Head.* 18 November 1960. Charcoal on corrugated cardboard, 22½ × 28⅜″ (57 × 72 cm)

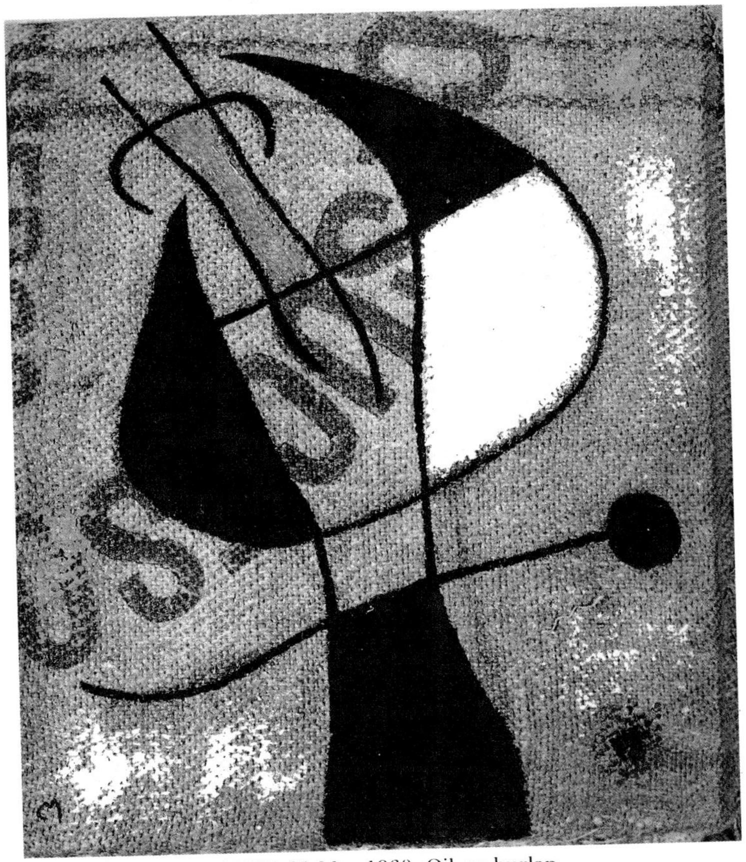

208. *Woman and Bird IX/X.* 30 May 1960. Oil on burlap, 16⅛ × 13⅛″ (41 × 33.5 cm)

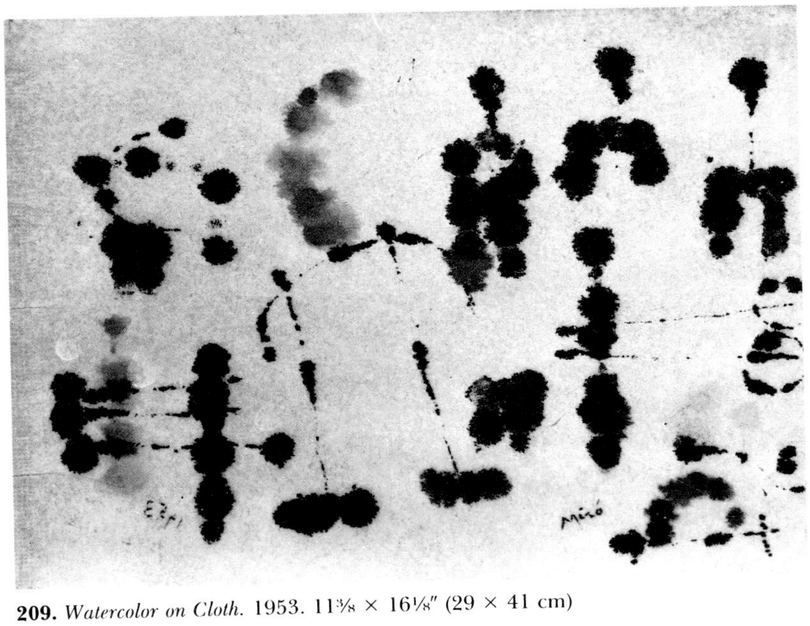

209. *Watercolor on Cloth.* 1953. 11⅜ × 16⅛″ (29 × 41 cm)

210. *Heads (Flag).* 3 June 1960. Oil on frayed canvas, 19⅝ × 27⅝″ (50 × 70 cm)

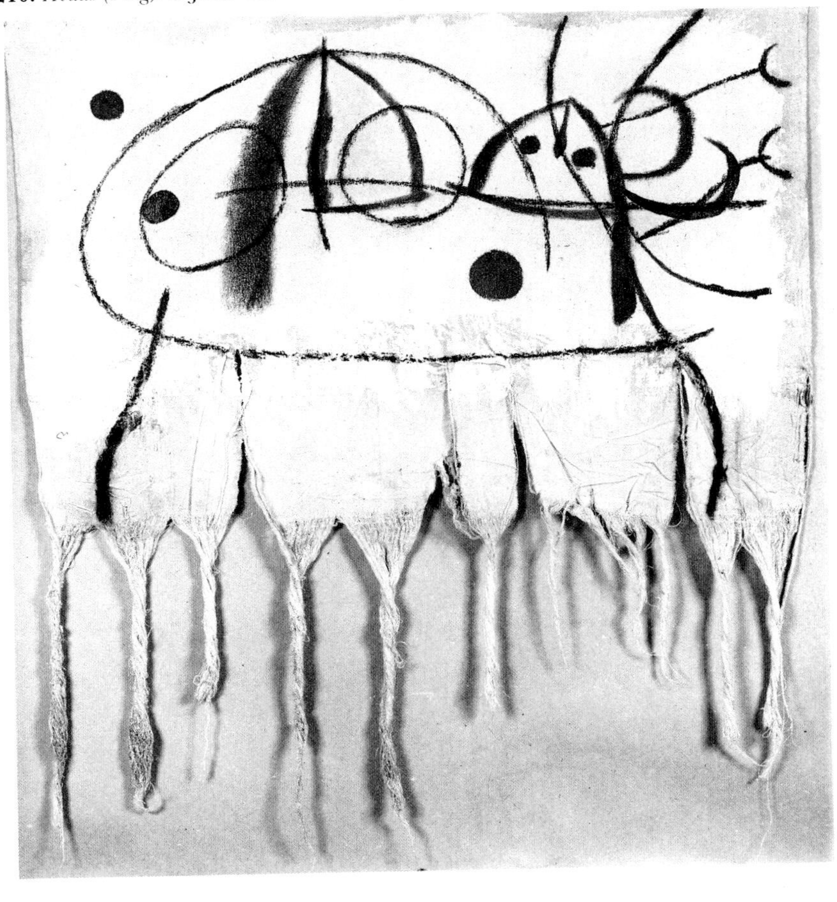

211. *Painting.* 1953. Oil on canvas, 78 × 28¾" (198 × 73 cm)

212. *Hair Disheveled by the Fleeing Constellations.* 19 January 1954.
Oil on canvas, 51⅛ × 71⅝" (130 × 182 cm). Private collection, Paris

213. *Painting.* 1954. Oil on canvas, 18⅛ × 15" (46 × 38 cm).
Fundació Miró, Barcelona

214. *Painting (The Wind).* 1953. Oil on canvas, 76¾ × 38⅛"
(195 × 97 cm). Private collection, Barcelona

215. *Hope Returns to Us with the Flight of the Constellations.*
2 October 1954. Oil on canvas, 44⅞ × 57½" (114 × 146 cm)

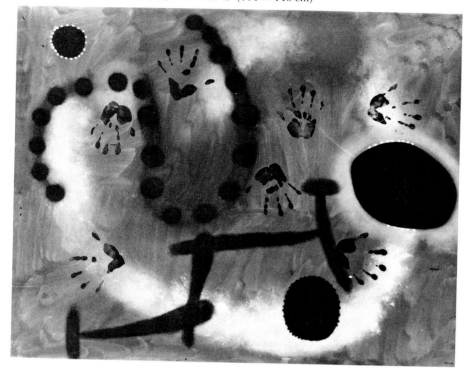

Paintings of 1955

Miró did not need to stop and marshal his forces; questions and doubts could be answered through work. The ten or so small canvases of 1955 (plate 216), practically the last for that decade, presented both a sudden leap and an about-face. Again the forms gesticulate at will, the colors flash against a light ground; all the canvases arise from a single frame of mind, from the same clear hand. To break his indecision, Miró returned to his favorite means, which had proved their worth. He knew their handling and capabilities down to his fingertips. Despite their small dimensions, these canvases are monumental and impressive.

Part of 1956 was taken up with a move to Palma de Majorca. For twenty years, Miró had been dreaming of a large studio. On a steep hill overlooking the beach of Calamayor, his longtime friend the architect Josep Luis Sert built for him an ensemble of spaces where he finally could work without constraints, each room having its particular purpose. For all his professed indifference to the material conditions of lighting, Miró found this aspect difficult to adapt to these new quarters. Then there was a labyrinth of majestic spaces and open terraces that had to be learned physically, surveyed step by step. Not only did he have to learn the new space, he also had to distribute his pictures, make choices among them, put them in

order, arrange works in progress still calling for attention, align or turn to the wall the virgin surfaces whose brilliant whiteness could sometimes itself be a threat. He busied himself furnishing those great open spaces with all the objects his keen eye lighted on during his walks.

Soon his things themselves turned inquisitorial. Finally, he undertook to sort out his files, review his drawings and notebooks, classify baskets full of notes and cartons of scattered papers accumulated since childhood and preserved with foresight. All of his life passed before his eyes. The interrogations became more pressing, a squalling mob demanding to have its needs and claims listened to. In the solitude of his studios, still without heat, swept from time to time by capricious gusts from the Mediterranean wind that drew growls from the sea, Miró felt himself drawn to new adventures. He had many and varied avenues at his disposal. Among other things, Artigas was ready to give him whatever time he wanted, and there were persistent demands for editions of his prints. In spite of his difficulties, Miró pressed on. And, of course, his new experiences responded also to an old desire, whose time had come. "How to live without the unknown before one": René Char's fine phrase could have been written for Miró. For close to five years, he would now devote himself to lithography and ceramics.

160

216. *Graphism-Concert*. 1955. Oil on canvas, 29½ × 39⅜″ (75 × 100 cm)

Ceramics

Once again, the depth of Miró's attachment to his native soil and all it encompassed emerged. Before the inevitable advent of industrialization, Catalonia had had an authentic tradition of folk pottery. Peasants and city housewives alike made daily use of the local potters' products. The noble and ample ancestral forms of those utensils had long been fixed; even today, they are still respected in a few countryside workshops, although their production is aimed mostly at the tourist.

The urban type of decorated ceramics underwent great development at the start of this century, especially with Art Nouveau. Gaudí had the idea of using it systematically; the winding walls of Parque Güell and the superb fireplaces of his Casa Mila show with what inventive and decorative spirit he was able to put to new use the debris and discards of an important Barcelona pottery factory. These examples—along with his admiration for his old friend Artigas's craftsmanship—doubtless lie behind Miró's interest in seeing what he could do with ceramics (plates 217–22).

Unlike Picasso, who could not resist torturing the potter's freshly produced forms into new and unusual shapes, Miró was attracted by the simplicity and beauty of the traditional objects: vases with long or short necks and harmonious lines much like those of the ancient amphora, Catalan cups with sensual concavities, gently

curving plates—all these called for no more than the magic of his decoration. The beautiful material of an irregular plaque produced by Artigas, with wrinkled surface, resembling a brick from an Assyrian palace, or with skin as soft as a tomato's gorged with sunlight, needed nothing more than a nimble sign tattooed in brilliant colors.

Such elementary forms as an egg marked by an incision, a pottery pebble decorated with a simple star, or a fragment with an archaeological cast to it sufficed to stimulate Miró's archaic reverie, which arose from the same source as his Oriental sensibility.

For all the pertinent rigor of his submission to the pure form as handed down through the ages, Miró was incapable of not giving free rein to his imagination. Small figurines, composite personages, broken clay shards put to new use gave rise to numerous new shapes with a textured or smoothly glazed surface. However, he, too, tormented these shapes, by digging his finger into the still-soft clay, scratching the surface with a fingernail, mounting a mass on a three-legged stand, replacing a face with the fan of a scallop shell. To graffiti moldering within the collective unconscious he gave form, volume, and new meaning. Phenomena of a highly developed sensibility, these seem to touch on the dream territory of the naive oddities of art, the untrained aspirants after beauty who people

161

217. *Personage with Birds.* 1956. Ceramic, height 21⅝" (55 cm)

218. Ceramics on exhibit

219. *Large Vase.* 1966. Ceramic, 35⅜ × 19⅝″ (90 × 50 cm)

221. *Large Jar.* 1962. Ceramic, 28¾ × 17¾″ (73 × 45 cm)

220. *Vase.* 1962. Ceramic, height 4¾″ (12 cm)

163

222. *Anti-Plate.* 1956. Ceramic, diameter 19⅝″ (50 cm). The village of Gallifa is seen in the background

The Graphic Work

their suburban gardens with assorted nostalgic remnants.

With ceramics and lithography, Miró initiated what can be considered a new phase in his art. Retrospectives at the Museum of Modern Art, New York, and the Los Angeles County Museum, Los Angeles, gave Miró the opportunity to revisit the United States. The major event of his stay, which would have important consequences, was the ceremony of 18 May 1959 in the White House, when President Eisenhower awarded him the international grand prize of the Guggenheim Foundation for his ceramic walls at the UNESCO headquarters in Paris (plate 177).

Miró's extensive graphic work is studded with flashes of inspiration, what he himself called "sparks" (plates 223–32). A medium that permitted him to make changes on a plate, to replace one image with another—even to ruin the whole thing—doubtless made it easy for him to give voice to both his sense of rigorous order and his spontaneous impulse. It also returned him to the pleasure of teamwork, which demands from each participant his knowledge and technical know-how and offers to all the emotion of discovery and the joy of an idea developed in common taking place under the common gaze. René Lemoigne, a specialist in lithography who

223. *"Six Patiences pour Joan Miró"* by René Char. c. 1948. Embellished manuscript from the Jean Hughes collection, 13 × 20⅛″ (33 × 51 cm). Reproduced in *Le Monde de l'art n'est pas le monde du pardon*, Paris: Maeght Éditeur, 1948

worked with Miró, bears witness: "I give him a zinc plate and he takes off very freely, very fast, with an extraordinary rapidity. He uses no special instrument unless it be a natural instrument, the finger. He gets a lot of transparency and wash effects with the finger." In engraving, a medium in which one has to overcome the resistance of the metal, Robert Dutrou, another technician of the team, reports, "He has to have all his instruments, all his tools. He uses little knives, little tools that belong to him, that he spent years finding." Miró confirmed this: "I employ nonclassical instruments…this fork might help me to find a line." " 'Look,' he said, pointing to a tiny drop on the table, 'this point, shining as it does, produces a shock in me, and with that shock I can make an entire world' " (Yvon Taillandier, "Miró et ses équipes," *XXe Siècle: Hommage à Joan Miró*, special issue, 1972).

Miró finds the world that sets his imagination vibrating where no one victimized by cultural platitudes cares to look: under his feet, on the ground. A sardine tin, still with its key, crushed out of shape under the wheels of a car, a piece of scrap iron, a cylinder head still smelling of gasoline, a flattened length of barbed wire, a metal frame—all may leave on the engraving plate the poignant traces of debris rescued from oblivion. To find them, Miró did not have to dig them out—they simply fell into his hands. Gift of the poet-seer, mystery of encounters: every object he found was already a Miró,

eliminating the idea of chance. In this, Miró has often been imitated, even plagiarized. But with him, the objects seem to offer themselves, to meet him halfway, and that is why the works to which he gave his image strike us so clearly as inevitable.

This innate inventiveness, fed by his daily reading of the poets and listening to music, both early and contemporary, was accompanied by an invaluable rigor of method, perhaps even a ritual. He worked following a particular order, a sequence that stimulated his imagination, and he achieved results through extended hard work. Each interruption to his concentration must have struck him as an assault, but even these his diabolical agility, in the effort to find the way back to the guiding idea, sometimes managed to turn to unexpected profit.

Such receptiveness, pushed to a virtue, made him particularly adapted to embellish the books of his poet friends. The task called for knowing how to grasp the rhythms, the chiming of words, the way the phrases breathed, and the sense of space in the works of poets as different as André Breton, René Char, Cabral de Melo, Jacques Dupin, Paul Éluard, Michel Leiris, Raymond Queneau, and others. For each he had to find the appropriate coloristic counterpoint in which, by a kind of leapfrog, his contribution actually facilitated the reading of the poem, extending it into the realm of color. Miró never illustrated in the usual sense of the word

224. *Graphism, Poem, Bird.* 1951. 27⅝ × 39⅜" (70 × 10 cm)

225–32. *L'Auca d'Ubu.* After Alfred Jarry. c. 1972. Brush, India ink, colored pencils, each 12⅞ × 19¾" (32.7 × 50.2 cm). Fundació Miró, Barcelona

nor followed the development of a text word for word. Instead, he interpreted. He began with the page as a whole, its typographical layout, and through it established a circuit of sparkling signs, running currents, and eddies. His inherent sense of perfect color placement led to marvelous results; the colored parade he invented around René Char's "Six Patiences pour Joan Miró" (plate 223) is an exemplary success.

Were they not so numerous, all his works for poets would deserve study here. One of them, however, merits particular attention: Alfred Jarry, author among other things of *Ubu Roi* and *Le Surmâle*, whose grating verve struck a note of affinity in Miró and thoroughly seduced him. Rosa Maria Malet supposes that the artist discovered the work of Jarry as early as 1924, through his Surrealist friends. Poetry had been a familiar world to him from his early years, and his curiosity ranged from the hermetic sonnets of Luis de Góngora, for example, to the audacious writings of his own generation. In 1963, he invented *Ubu aux Baléares*, a book for which he collected "humorous and vulgar phrases from Catalan and Majorcan popular speech appropriate to Ubu's character" (this and subsequent quotations from Rosa Maria Malet, "L'Auca d'Ubu," in *Dessins de Miró*, exhibition catalogue, 1978–79). In 1937, he contributed several drawings to an illustrated version of *Ubu Enchaîné;* in 1966, he produced thirteen lithographs for a collector's edition of *Ubu Roi;* in 1975, there was *L'Enfance d'Ubu;* and, around 1972, never published but included in the archives of his foundation in Barcelona, he prepared a new version of Jarry's famous play. For this he chose a form, the *auca*, "with deep roots in his native land, Catalonia." The narration is "accompanied by a series of drawings which, as in the comic strips of nowadays, proceed from left to right and from top to bottom" (plates 225–32).

Using drawing paper of the same dimensions and numbering the sheets in sequence, Miró drew images that, whether they followed or departed from the text, always retained its acerbic character. In the very subtle analysis in which Rosa Maria Malet distinguishes

between real, hypothetical, hypothetically real, and oneiric time, she finds that Miró took pleasure in playing "freely with time … and showed … everything it would be impossible for us to catch visually in the theater." Since Jarry had been careful to specify that "as for the action, it takes place in Poland, which is to say nowhere," Miró followed his stricture, and so "we see the personages drawn … without any topographical reference in most cases. We make out only from time to time a few geographical and architectural allusions that have only a purely referential value, never specific." Finally, the figures are based "chiefly on the letter *U*, the first letter of the protagonist's name." "These 'Mirónian' personages are archetypes: they have an interchangeable value which makes possible all the necessary combinations." The letter *U* is found "in the place where there should be the arm, nose or mouth of a personage [or] silhouetting the windmill or, elsewhere, the contour of a mountain."

This exploration of the grotesque personage of Ubu was given full rein in *Mori el Merma*, a scathing spectacle performed by La Claca Teatre group, "whose personages, dressed in white cotton and foam rubber" colored by Miró himself, come directly out of the pages of *L'Auca d'Ubu*, making a fitting coda to Miró's fifty-year preoccupation with Ubu.

What the Surrealists and Miró with them admired above all in Jarry's youthful farce (not really a well-made play) was the grotesquerie of the situations, the provocative language, and the derision heaped on established institutions and values: on churches, armies, politics, and all the hypocritical niceties that respectable society tries to impose and perpetuate at any cost. In time, it became obvious that, for Miró, behind Ubu was concealed General Franco in particular and fascism in general. Over and beyond Jarry's sexual violence, of which Miró, as in a flight of mirrors, found himself the reflection, there is also the Catalan claim of independence and the painter's own fundamental, organic hatred of the oppressor.

166

225. *Père Ubu Holding a "Gidouille"*

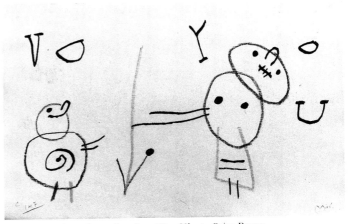

226. *Mère Ubu Tries to Convince Père Ubu to Seize Power*

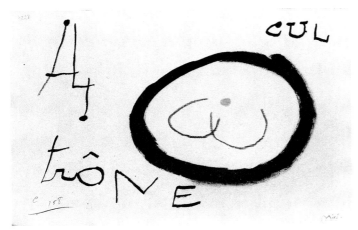

227. *Père Ubu's Ass*

228. *Père Ubu Grabbing a Chicken*

229. *Père Ubu Changing Horses*

230. *Père Ubu, Now King, Arguing with Mère Ubu*

231. *Père Ubu Gives the Signal to Murder the King of Poland*

232. *Père Ubu Dragging His Horse by the Bridle*

167

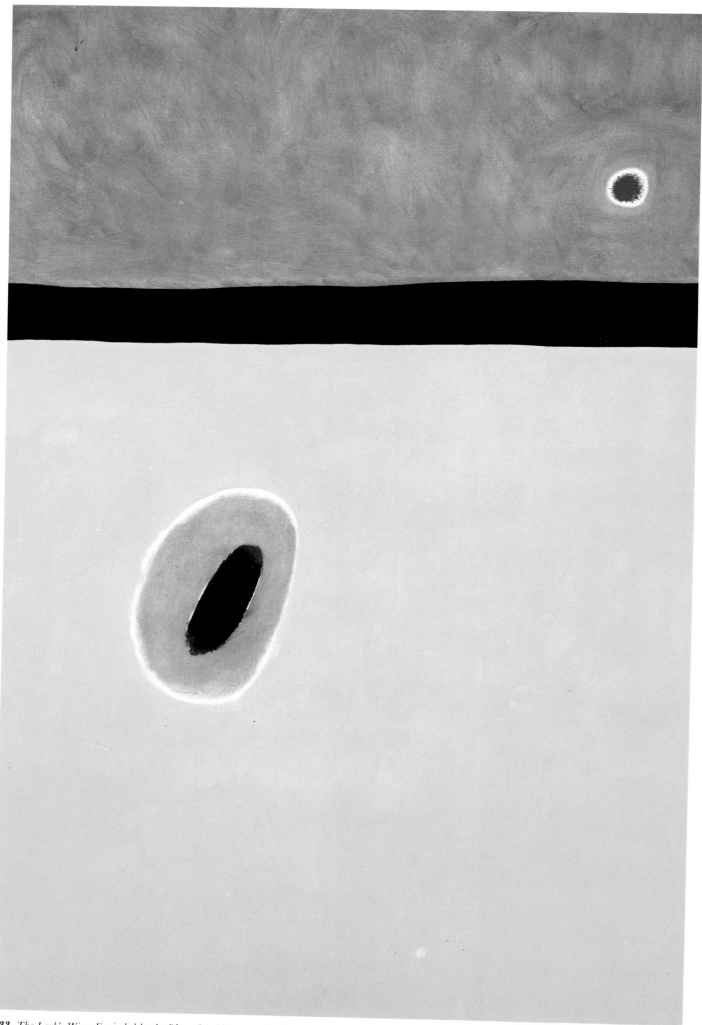

233. *The Lark's Wing Encircled by the Blue of Gold Rejoins the Heart of the Poppy Sleeping on the Meadow Bedecked with Diamonds.*
13 March 1967. Oil on canvas, 76¾ × 51⅛″ (195 × 130 cm)

"I do not rule out the possibility that in looking at one of my pictures, a businessman might discover the means to make a deal, a scientist the means to solve a problem. The solution constituted by a picture is a solution of a general order applicable to all sorts of areas." —TO YVON TAILLANDIER

Miró had been much impressed by the United States on his first visit in 1947. He was struck by that strange feeling of immensity that comes over every sensitive and open-minded visitor from the Old World. Suddenly, one's normal scale is overwhelmed; instantly, everything becomes enormous. In America, too, Miró had reunited with his painter friends, Parisian by birth or choice, who had chosen to emigrate for a variety of reasons but who all shared a deep loathing of fascism. He came into contact with many painters, visited a number of studios, exhibitions, art galleries. The younger generation of American artists clearly had already found matter for reflection in his work and had exploited it, even, as in the case of Jackson Pollock, for example, as a primary influence (Jackson Pollock, *Arts and Architecture* 61, February 1944, pp. 14–15).

The effervescent give-and-take of New York intellectual life could not help but grip Miró. Certain ideas of the proponents of the "new American painting," which Paris would not discover until 1951–52, ran along lines on which he had been thinking. In particular, many affinities can be noted between the sources, predilections, inclinations, and working methods of Miró and Jackson Pollock, one of the strongest presences of his generation. What the latter said of his way of working could have served for Miró as well: "My painting does not come from the easel. I hardly ever stretch my canvas before painting. I prefer to tack the unstretched canvas to the hard wall or the floor. I need the resistance of a hard surface. On the floor I am more at ease. I feel nearer, more a part of the painting, since this way I can walk around it, work from the four sides and literally be *in* the painting.... I continue to get further away from the usual painter's tools such as easel, palette, brushes, etc. I prefer sticks, trowels, knives, and dripping fluid paint or a heavy impasto with sand, broken glass, and other foreign matter added" ("My Painting," *Possibilities* 1, Winter 1947, p. 79). Without doubt, Pollock's observations, like his personal reflections, confirm his independence from the cultural forms that belong to Europe in general and Paris in particular.

It should be remarked here that all art remains dependent on a

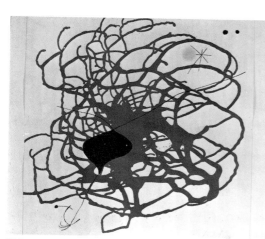

234. Project for a poster:
"Pour les États Généraux du Coeur."
21 June 1966

235. *Woman's Head and Bird on a Fine Blue Day.*
27 March 1963. Oil on cardboard,
40⅜ × 29½" (102.5 × 75 cm)

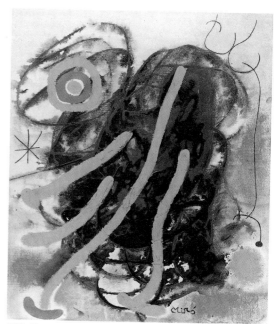

236. *Personage, Bird, Star.* 5 July 1965. Oil on canvas,
16⅛ × 13" (41 × 33 cm)

particular space and light as well as on a history and a society to which it is intimately linked and which it ends up influencing. All painting, all artistic expression whose language is sufficiently rich and fertile finally surpasses the frontiers of its birthplace. It becomes international by virtue of its delving into profound collective concerns and yet remains regional. "The idea of an isolated American painting…seems absurd to me, just as the idea of creating a purely American mathematics or physics would seem absurd.…An American is an American and his painting would naturally be qualified by that fact, whether he wills it or not. But the basic problems of contemporary painting are independent of any one country" (Jackson Pollock, *Arts and Architecture* 61, February 1944, p. 14).

To signal the opening up that occurred in Miró's work, Dupin identifies as "spontaneous" a series of works created in 1949–50 and distinguishes them from other paintings of the same years that he labeled "slow." But it was in the mediums of ceramics, which occupied Miró from 1953, and lithography, which he took up soon afterward, that the signs of this stubborn and increasingly explosive quest for a new freedom first began to take form. His travels in 1959 and 1961, with their new contacts, afforded him a greater acquaintance with what was going on, and, given the time to turn the new information into exemplary new works of his own, confirmed his ideas. "It is one of the ironies of art history that the new American painting impressed Miró, for he himself was an important catalyst in its formation" (Rowell, *Miró*, 1968, p. 19). But such constant exploring should be viewed as the most natural reaction and the legitimate right of any artist and human being. Irony enters into it only if there is a feeling of superiority and, on one side, of national superiority, a feeling that has, in fact, perverted the relations between European and American artists since Impressionism.

Matisse declared that a particular sensibility prevails in a period and often ignores geography, but one should go even further and think of a veritable Pentecost of ideas. Even if ideas crystallize around the same considerations, in different latitudes and individuals they will never be quite the same and their consequences will differ. With time, each person adapts them to particular needs, whether personal, local, cultural, historical, or social.

After World War II, people's relationships to the world changed. The cannons and planes had slaughtered more than human beings, destroyed more than cities. Many values and beliefs likewise collapsed. Like some other artists, Miró asked questions of himself. The act of painting itself was questioned, taken apart, dissected, and it ended by becoming the central fact in itself. Painstaking slow work, long considered one of the laws of good artistic practice, was violently contested, and the weight of culture was again disparaged, this time in the name of speed and immediacy. Broad gesture and bodily energy became the new measure and rhythm. Traditionally dense and closed, form became open, lacerated. The freedom being tested in younger lands was in revolt against the ancient geometry, more or less a closed system, which, in those years, was still in full sway in Europe. Perspective, already fully dethroned, collapsed into apparent obsolescence. The picture surface reasserted its authority. The "inner necessity" that Kandinsky cherished—without defining who was to judge it—became a fundamental criterion. The surreal instant had to be either a lightning stroke or nothing. Intensity of sensation, with all its violence, claimed supremacy. Shock, too, had its rationale and perhaps even a logic.

Thick or fluid paint was blithely and energetically flung onto the canvas from brushes, tins, or trowels. Without previous plan, colors were splashed on in squirts and spurts. Any and every material was urged to make a molten lava. The old problems of space and time, which had haunted painters since painting began, were being

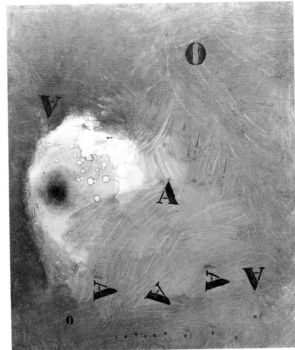

237. *Burnt Canvas I.* 1973. Oil on torn
and burnt canvas, 51⅛ × 76¾"
(130 × 195 cm). Fundació Miró, Barcelona

238. *Letters and Numbers Drawn to a Spark.* 5 June 1968.
Oil on canvas, 57½ × 44⅞" (146 × 114 cm)

239. *The Passage of the Migratory Bird.*
29 January 1968. Oil on canvas,
76¾ × 51⅛" (195 × 130 cm)

formulated in new terms. To the groups working in Europe was
added Art Informel, inaugurated in Paris by Michel Tapié: the
American experiments had crossed the ocean and once again took
the guise of insistent interrogations of reality, which, for scientists as
well as artists, allows one to approach it before it inevitably escapes.
The ruthless experiment of Art Informel proved salutary; the
vehemence of the confrontations suddenly made it possible to open
current ideas to debate, to flush out what was already in danger of
becoming a cultural code of rules and principles. In an ambiguous
article on Art Informel, Jean Paulhan wrote: "The informal has at
least the merit of exposing the most evident approach of a painter
who begins by evading every rule and established figure—every
form taken as such. So that if eventually his work gives birth to new
forms, at least he can honestly say he had nothing to do with it....
If the painter aspires to a rapidity that cuts short all reflection, if he
refuses the help of instruments that weigh down his thinking such
as the brush or pencil, if he evades every intention, and, should he
not entirely shirk a meaning, if he renders (or receives) it in so
confused and muddled a state that the art lover (and the painter
himself) cannot get the point, nevertheless it seems that we are
witnessing a perfectly coherent undertaking which aims to drive out
of art all a priori approach, all reasoning, all opinion" ("L'Art
informel [éloge]," *Nouvelle Revue Française*, May 1961, pp. 792–93).

Nonetheless, the most contradictory types of painting continued
to exist and coexist in Paris, the city that quickly catches fire but
never burns for long and welcomes if not accepts all divergences. It
was in Paris, in March 1952, when Paul Facchetti boldly organized a
first solo exhibition for Jackson Pollock, that Miró seems to have
recognized what he himself was heading toward. Margit Rowell
reported that Miró found the exhibition a "revelation" (*Joan Miró:
Magnetic Fields*, exhibition catalogue, 1972, p. 64, note 56). Still, in
1977, when asked what he thought of Pollock, Miró replied: "As a

point of departure I find it works very well, but it remains limited.
I have a great respect for him, I like him very much. But one
shouldn't just remain there. He himself felt it and he committed
suicide" (to Georges Raillard, 1977, p. 97).

Miró has always tried to express himself with the minimum of
means required to obtain the maximum of intensity. This
temptation of austerity is the perhaps necessary contradiction of a
hunger for freedom which, in painting, may express itself within
orderly limits or push beyond those limits. A Mediterranean, Miró
held a long-term dialogue with the exotic sign that tended to bring
him into harmony with the Far East. The old painters of China
and, later, Japan, with their ascetic commitment, often relied on the
simple and admirable powers of white and black to arrive at a total
identification with the gesture in which all the forces of the universe
become absorbed. Beauty as we conceive it was neither their
principle nor the essential aim. Rather, through the silence of
inward powers, through absence, the calligrapher could succeed in
becoming one with what our vocabulary calls harmony. The self
(still employing our terminology) passes out of itself like light, and
then unity becomes perceptible. As the sages put it, one attains "the
other shore of the ocean of being in the heart of ourselves" (R.
Linssen, *Le Zen, Sagesse d'Extrême-Orient: un nouvel art de vivre?*, Paris:
Verviers, Gerard, 1969, p. 8).

Without being a confirmed authority on Far Eastern
philosophical disciplines, Miró pushed that experience far. Striking
among his work are a few difficult and admirable canvases in which
a simple line, a point, a spot succeeds in coexisting with a light
ground, vibrant as the myriad reflections on the surface of water
(plates 239–45). Their significance may remain enigmatic, but their
tension rises to the surface, coexisting with a harmony that prolongs
itself and settles in: pacified, mysterious. Our words and syntax are
inadequate tools to measure the density of what is other than mere

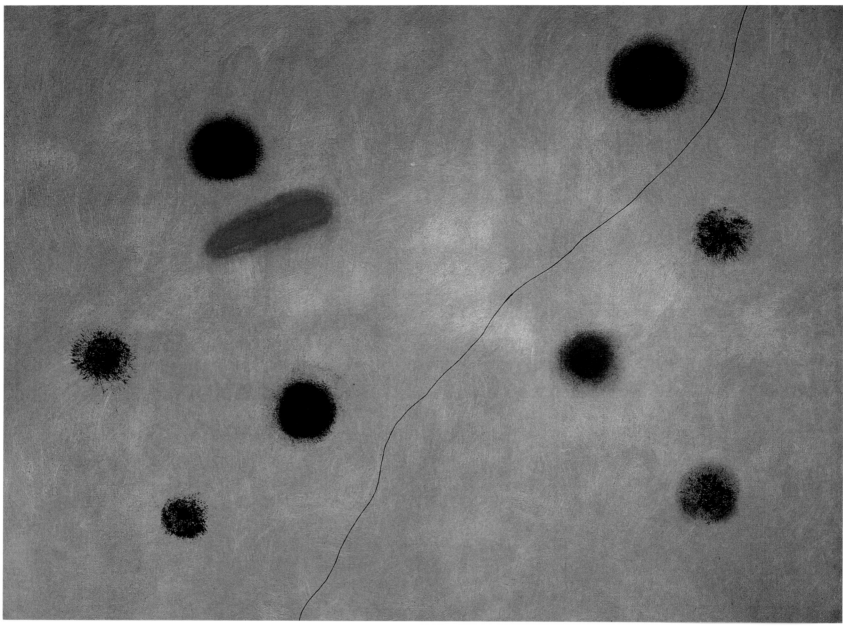

240. *Blue I*. 4 March 1961. Oil on canvas, 8′ 10¼″ × 11′ 7¾″ (2.7 × 3.55 m). Galerie Maeght, Paris

241–43. *Triptych: The Hope of a Man Condemned to Death I, II, III*. 1974. Oil on canvas, each panel 8′ 10¼″ × 11′ 7⅜″ (2.7 × 3.54 m). Fundació Miró, Barcelona

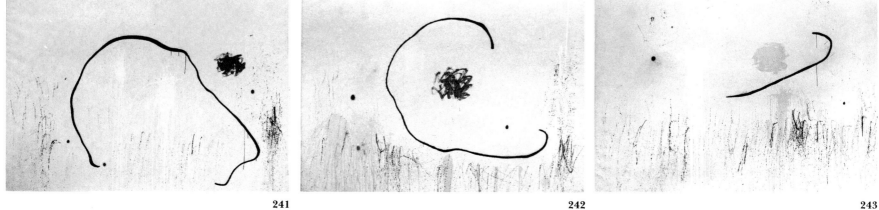

241   242   243

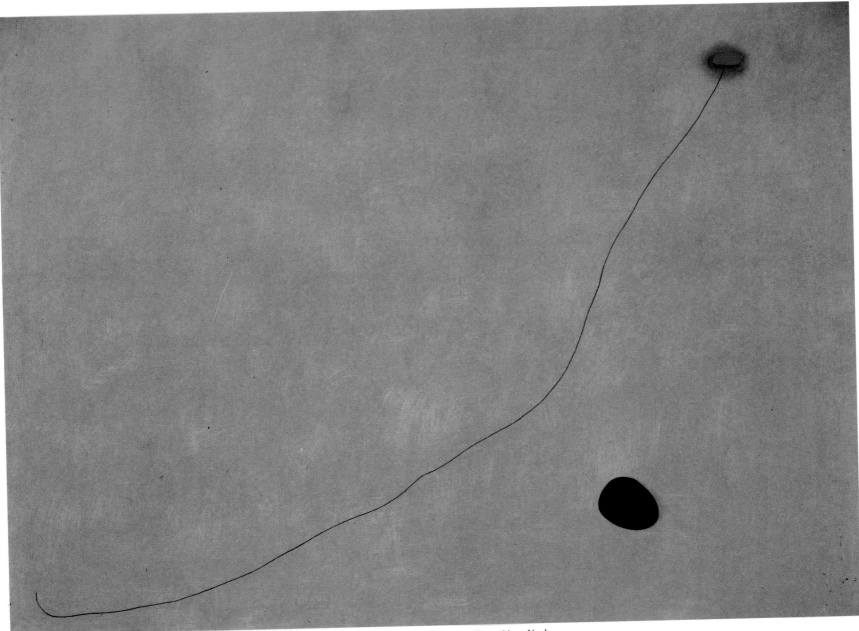

244. *Blue III*. 4 March 1961. Oil on canvas, 8'10¼" × 11'7¾" (2.7 × 3.55 m). Pierre Matisse Gallery, New York

245. *Triptych: Fireworks I, II, III*. 1974. Oil on canvas, 9'7" × 19'2¾" (2.92 × 5.86 m). Fundació Miró, Barcelona

246. *Head.* 1940–74. Oil on canvas, 25⅝ × 19⅝″ (65 × 50 cm).
Fundació Miró, Barcelona

247. *Woman in Front of the Moon.* 1974. Oil on canvas,
8′9⅞″ × 5′8½″ (2.69 × 1.74 m). Fundació Miró, Barcelona

image, our minds poorly prepared to penetrate its meaning.

In truth, an Occidental nourished from birth on very different cultural fare will never known in the flesh the successive experiences of the senses that work on the body as much as they fashion the mind, even if intellectually he succeeds in apprehending those philosophical teachings. "Zen, Taoism, Buddhism are the ultimate issue of an evolution of human thought realized in a psychological climate completely different from ours by peoples whose sensibility, ways of thinking, and sense of values are unfamiliar to us" (Linssen, *Le Zen*, pp. 7–8). Everything the mind experiences originates as an experience of the body, and that is perhaps one of the profound significations of Miró's work. In other terms, body and mind, artificially disjoined in the Judeo-Christian tradition, fundamentally send information back and forth. Perhaps we are seeing appear what, for all the genuineness of our desire, remains definitively incommunicable between human beings as well as between cultures—for example, between West and East.

After 1960, at the same time that he was occupied with numerous projects for which he had assumed responsibility, Miró turned inward to attain by extreme freedom and renunciation that "electric" instant in which gesture itself takes on all colors, all resonances. At such an instant, it acts without being weighed down by consciousness or thought and seeks to be as unconstrained as possible. This explains why his works of those decades are open to such different and ambiguous interpretations.

In trying to follow Miró in these works with some possibility of drawing close to him, the only revealing commentary would probably be a long, difficult, perhaps even exhausting and unreadable study of the facts, that is, of the actual practice of his painting. In what way and at what moment and how, with regard to the demands of a blank canvas or of the first spot of paint applied, did the painter lay on his color or, in ceramics, spread his colored glaze on a plaque? In what way and at what moment does a point or line come into being? Such a description would call for inventing a new way of writing, one subject to a different structure. But let us have no illusions: to subscribe to such questions would be to uncover the unexpected mask assumed by an intuition, a particular set of mind. What is remote should remain so, perhaps even be beyond reach, and only the ambiguity of poetry can bring us a little closer.

For all that, in his painting Miró did not totally abandon his faithful companions: birds, stars, disheveled women, sex organs flying through the azure or stuck in macadam (plates 246–48). But they, too, would bear the mark of those new efforts. They plunge to the eyes into a black ever more present, an opaque, heavy, thick black that hides their dance. Like a theater curtain that has just dropped, this all-invading black conceals from us the unbridled agitation on the stage: another metaphor for austerity and freedom pushed to the limit. If all his familiars disappear in a cloak of night, at the same time, Miró himself escaped through sculpture.

174

248. *Catalan Peasant by Moonlight.* 26 March 1968. Oil on canvas, 63¾ × 51⅛″ (162 × 130 cm). Fundació Miró, Barcelona

250. *Sobreteixim No. 3.* 1972. 5′5″ × 9′6⅛″ (1.65 × 2.9 m)

252. *Tapestry on Coarse Cloth*

251. *Head.* 3 March 1972

253. *Sobreteixim-Sack.* 1973

254. *Sobreteixim-Sack.* 1973.
70⅞ × 21⅝" (180 × 55 cm)

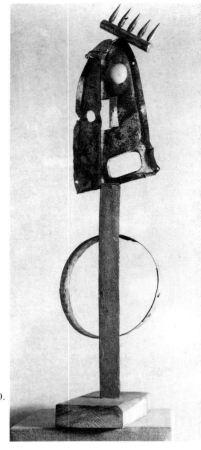

255. *Sculpture-Object.* 1950.
Wood and metal,
27⅜ × 6¾ × 1⅛"
(70 × 17 × 3 cm)

Tapestry

Traditionally utilized by nomads to serve as walls and to construct a space, then in castles and royal courts to dress the high chambers, suddenly around 1962 tapestry challenged those old uses. The great Polish artist Magdalena Abakanowicz covered walls with the anguish of Macbeth in the guise of reliefs and cascades woven out of sisal, ropes, twisted rags, braided horsehair. Once set on that path, tapestry soon took its freedom and finally stopped serving walls to become a sculpture of fibers, woven forms, knitted phantoms.

Miró treated tapestry much as he constructed objects: he painted and splattered frayed rags, he planted and fastened umbrellas, varicolored cloths, wickerwork, and ropes soaked in paint on rough surfaces. Then, going back to traditional weaving, he took it apart and reworked it to get the maximum effect out of entanglements, superpositions with disordered hairs, bunched-up areas, thick tufts of wool and threads (plates 249–54). As the large-scale tapestry *Woman* (plate 249) shows, he worked the textile like a sculptor modeling the surface of a bas-relief, in turn building up the full parts, digging out hollows, and—because he remained, as always, a painter—accentuating it all by the violent effects of brilliant colors.

Sculptures

Ever since ancient times, when sculpture first became an autonomous means of expression, it has taken the form of one or more articulated volumes set in space and exposed to light, and thereby subject to effects and contrasts of light and shadow. By his express intention, Miró's sculptural works (plates 255–67) are indifferent to that overly classical principle. There, as in other activities, he deliberately turned his back on established principles. Nor was it for him a matter of simply taking the opposite course: to be against implies a dependence on the same principles, even if many artists take this simple way of simulating independence. Miró looked elsewhere. Of his sculptures, Jacques Dupin aptly asked: "Of what 'elsewhere' are they native, of what realm of the fantastic are they the voyagers?" (*Miró: Cent sculptures*, exhibition catalogue, 1978). In the same catalogue, Dupin called these works "assemblage sculptures," and Dean Swanson reported the artist as saying: "It is a matter of the improbable marriage of recognizable forms. In most of the sculptures diverse objects are combined."

We have remarked more than once on Miró's gift for the marvelous and on the always mysterious theme of the encounter. It is as if objects were attracted by his presence and congregated at the sides of the roads where his steps might lead him. He did not watch for things but simply gathered them, did not seek but was made welcome, as if awaited. The delicacy of his playlike constructions results from the unforeseeable alliance of objects never meant to live together. Such seemingly absurd juxtaposition has much in common with absentminded lapses. But while those happen when

256. *Project for a Monument for Barcelona.* 1967.
Bronze, 52 × 11¾ × 9″ (132 × 30 × 23 cm)

257. *Clock of the Wind.* 1967. Bronze, 19¼ × 11¾ × 6¼″
(49 × 30 × 16 cm). Fundació Miró, Barcelona

258. *Personage.* 1956. Wood, ceramic, bone, and iron,
27⅝ × 9¼ × 11″ (70 × 23.5 × 28 cm). Private collection, Paris

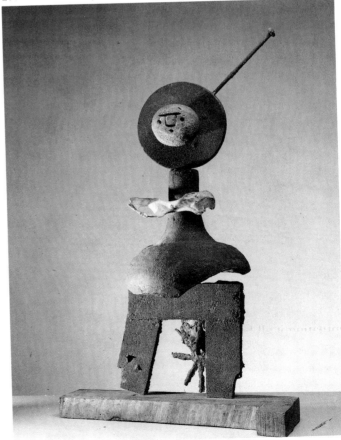

attention fails, with Miró it is the expression of an intuition and a slowly formed resolution. In his assemblages, he demonstrates almost casually that mere disdain for established principles will not open the way to the forgotten realm and that every transgression is above all psychological. An artist is impelled to modify the paths of communication because he cannot simply follow those already laid down. He does not accept the world as it is. The eye's habits, all those admirable certitudes, those rock-solid acquisitions raise up high palisades that block the view of the no-man's-land where Miró feels at home.

The force and vitality of his sculptures stem from the fact that these beings, these mechanisms, these strange hybrid creatures belong to no single class but to many, are ageless but of the past as well as the future, and are by nature incongruous, anomalous. The gaps between the object-forms function like relays in an electrical network, and when a short circuit occurs, sparks fly. Almost all these hybrids carry fire and, along with it, a question. But while the way they are put together serves to formulate that question, once they come into being, the names of all the objects composing them slip instantly from mind, and all that matters is the answer. The ill-assorted or ill-proportioned shapes they assume seem to obey a watchworks precision, and they somehow seem fit for a frenetic reproduction. It is then that they become menacing, and one cannot even picture the upside-down world they inhabit.

For one arrogant and rowdy *Bird (Lunar)* (plate 266), there are all those other tiny creatures salvaged from the gutter, destitute,

259. *Personage and Bird.* 1968. Bronze, 41 × 25¼ × 7⅛"
(104 × 64 × 18 cm)

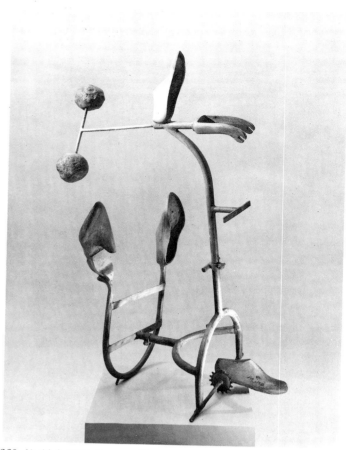

260. *Untitled.* 1974. Bronze, 37⅜ × 18½ × 19⅝" (95 × 47 × 50 cm)

261. *Personage.* 1970. Bronze, 78¾ × 47¼ × 39⅜"
(200 × 120 × 100 cm)

262. *Monsieur and Madame.* 1969. Painted bronze, 26¾ × 15 × 15"
and 39⅜ × 12¼ × 12¼" (68 × 38 × 38 and 100 × 31 × 31 cm)

263. *Père Ubu.* 1974. Painted synthetic resin,
70⅞ × 59 × 57⅛" (180 × 150 × 145 cm)

touching, pitiful, like the *Personage and Bird* of 1968 (plate 259), with its flattened basketwork. The bizarre contraption of 1974 (plate 260) seems to have been put together according to the disconcerting laws reshaped by Raymond Roussel for the enchanter in his *Locus Solus*. It could well preside at the meetings of the wags who joined in the "Ouvroir de Littérature Potentielle," the academy once founded by Raymond Queneau, past master in such exhilarating cocktails. The tortures Queneau's "Oulipistes" applied to assemblages of words to distort them and give them new breath went well beyond the refinements, however rare and complex, of the Elizabethan and Baroque poets, those princes of the hermetic. Miró, after all, had as companion of his quiet hours the poems of Góngora, the most renowned of the esoteric poets of Iberian literature (to Georges Raillard, 1977, p. 106).

The catalogue of Miró's sculpture up to 1978 in the excellent book by Alain Jouffroy and Joan Teixidor came to 237 items. From that abundance, one major project, which, in its largeness of spirit, seems to occupy a central position, stands out: a triumphal arch for the terraced gardens of the Fondation Maeght at Saint-Paul-de-Vence. The realization of Miró's *Labyrinth*, an outdoor space set with several sculptures of which the arch is one of the principal elements, occupied the artist for several years. This sculpture deliberately broke with the rash oddity of the sculpture-objects. For it, he made various maquettes, of which at least two were cast in bronze in 1962. The idea seems to have come from forms utilized in various circumstances in his paintings. It also appeared, although in schematic form, in the large-scale decorations for Harvard University and the Solomon R. Guggenheim Museum. The prefabricated cement arch recalls also a bronze *Woman* of 1949 and, with a few variations, the *Personage* of 1972 in painted synthetic resin (plate 264), as well as a project of the same year for a monument in Los Angeles.

Miró's usual terminology suggests that he was again juggling with the masculine and feminine genders so often interchangeable with him; the resources of ambiguity and ambivalence are inexhaustible. But these works all have in common the suggestion of a more or less widely open entrance into a cave; previously implied in his painting, it became realized in sculpture. The presence of a tunnel, of which only the opening is seen, remains implicit. In *Personage* of 1972 (plate 264), the enormous column-legs widen out at the foot, resembling leech suckers on the ground. The volumes of the arch are armed with tusks, rhinoceros horns, large balloons with pitted growths. Everything about the work proclaims that no one can pass its threshold unscathed. The "breast-mother" imagined by Guillaume Apollinaire has become too vindictive to let her progeny play with her "aeronautical" teats.

Gaston Bachelard has interpreted the symbolic meaning for the deep dreamer of such elements plunged in shadow: a corridor, a slide "in space—difficult path," which recall in the unconscious our first experience of passing from darkness to light. In a monstrous parturition, Miró's cruel divinity delivers anew to the world the traveler who unsuspectingly entered and became isolated in the *Labyrinth*, beneath whose bowers Miró concealed surprises and traps that lead to another kind of rebirth.

Despite all his later success, Miró never ceased to launch the most serious accusations against the world or forgot that he, for his part, was the object of a visceral rejection. He said, "I have become more and more a man of revolt. More and more, I revolt against the world as it is."

264

265

264. *Personage.* 1972. Painted synthetic resin, 7′4⅝″ × 11′3⅞″ × 5′3″ (2.25 × 3.45 × 1.6 m). In the background: *Monument.* 1970. Bronze, 98⅜ × 39⅜ × 19⅝″ (250 × 100 × 50 cm)

265. *Personage.* 1972. Painted synthetic resin, 6′9⅛″ × 9′5¾″ × 8′½″ (2.06 × 2.89 × 2.45 m)

266. *Bird (Lunar).* 1966. Bronze, 92⅛ × 82⅝ × 59″ (234 × 210 × 150 cm)

267. *Head.* 1978. Bronze, 72½ × 47¼ × 4¾″ (184 × 120 × 12 cm)

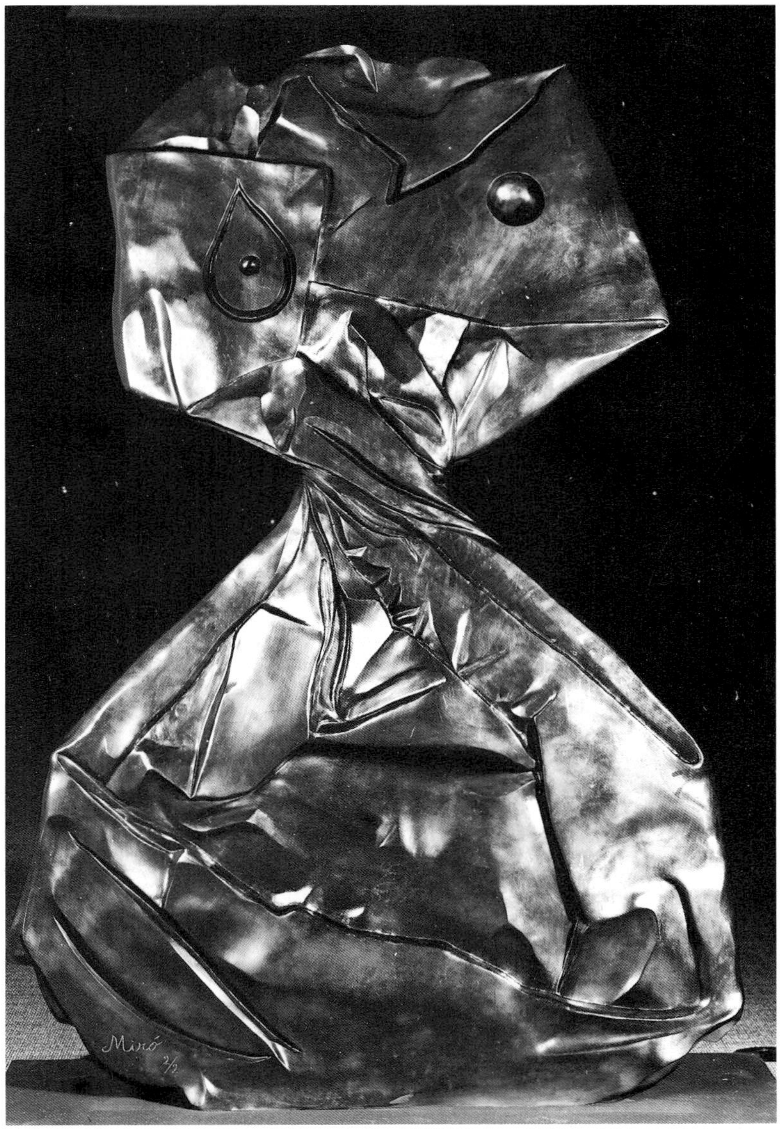

INDEX

PHOTOGRAPH CREDITS